The Indelible
Alison Bechdel

Other books by the author:

Hot, Throbbing Dykes To Watch Out For
Unnatural Dykes To Watch Out For
Spawn Of Dykes To Watch Out For
Dykes To Watch Out For: The Sequel
New, Improved! Dykes To Watch Out For
More Dykes To Watch Out For
Dykes To Watch Out For

The Indelible Alison Bechdel

Confessions, Comix, and Miscellaneous Dykes To Watch Out For

by Alison Bechdel

Firebrand
Books
Ithaca, New York

Book and cover design by Alison Bechdel and Debra Engstrom
Printed in Canada

10   9   8   7   6   5   4   3   2

Library of Congress Cataloging-in-Publication Data

Bechdel, Alison, 1960-
    The indelible Alison Bechdel : confessions, comix, and miscellaneous dykes to watch out for / by Alison Bechdel.
        p.   cm.
        ISBN 1-56341-097-4 (cloth : alk. paper). − ISBN 1-56341-096-6 (pbk. : alk. paper)
        1. Lesbians−Caricatures and cartoons. 2. American wit and humor, Pictorial.   I. Title
    NC1429.B3513A4   1998
    741.5'973−dc21
                                                            98-9305
                                                               CIP

For Amy Rubin. Editor, muse, sine qua non.

Contents

Preface

I actually make my living drawing a comic strip about a bunch of lesbians. That might not sound quite so improbable as it did fifteen, or even five years ago, but I never take it for granted.

In 1981 I was an aimless grad school reject, just out of college and trying to learn my way around New York City, where I'd ended up by default. One day I wandered into the Oscar Wilde Memorial Bookshop and picked up the first issue of *Gay Comix*. Though I loved to draw cartoony pictures, and I'd been out as a lesbian for a couple of years, the notion of cartoons about being gay had never crossed my mind.

The cover of this comic book featured an unusually well-favored lad about to fellate a hot dog dripping with mustard, but inside I found comics by women as well as men. There was wonderful work in that first issue by Lee Mars, Mary Wings, and Roberta Gregory, along with a beautifully drawn piece by the editor, Howard Cruse. In the next couple of issues I read work by Jennifer Camper, Kurt Erichsen, Robert Triptow, Cheela Smith, Jerry Mills, and others. Somewhere between issues 3 and 4 I started drawing my own cartoons.

I didn't find out until much later that Howard Cruse had struggled over the decision to draw gay-themed work after years as a successful underground cartoonist. Or that Mary Wings, who'd already published *Come Out Comix*, in 1977, had encouraged him to do it. There is groundbreaking work that

I've benefitted from but never even seen, like the first lesbian contribution (by a lesbian, anyway) to the underground anthology, *Wimmen's Comix*, that Roberta Gregory drew in 1974. When I stumbled into that bookstore in 1981, there was already such a thing as a lesbian cartoonist. I didn't have to invent it, or fight for it, or suffer over it. I just did it.

About This Book

In the fifteen years since I started drawing "Dykes To Watch Out For," I've amassed a modest heap of other cartoons that have not appeared in any of the seven *Dykes* collections published by Firebrand Books. Most of this is work that was commissioned by various publications and organizations, or that I created for anthologies. *The Indelible Alison Bechdel* collects much of this miscellaneous work, along with many of the cartoons that appeared in the annual calendar I did with Firebrand from 1990 to 1997.

Although only about half of the work compiled here is about the "Dykes To Watch Out For" characters, I think of this book as a companion to the collected strips. There's a section about the genesis and development of Mo, Lois, Clarice, Toni, et al. There's a handy chart plotting their backgrounds and critical episodes in their lives, such as the first and last times Mo and Harriet had sex, Clarice's little infidelity, and Lois's hairstyle shift. And I've included some of the comments these episodes have garnered from my perspicacious and demanding readers over the years.

This book also includes a lot of my own marginal commentary. The opportunity to explain what prompted a particular cartoon, exactly why the drawing sucks so bad in this one, or what my mother thought about that one, was too good to pass up.

Finally, what ideas I couldn't squeeze into the margins, I have written out in the form of essays. These are cleverly interspersed with the artwork to minimize their very uncartoonlike word-to-picture ratio.

One of my all-time favorite *Mad Magazine* cartoons began with a first-grader's "What I Did Last Summer" report about visiting a farm and seeing pigs. The cartoon goes on to show how the kid parlays this barely literate scrawl into a career as an expert in animal husbandry. Excerpts from his subsequent term papers, doctoral dissertation, journal articles, and books rephrase in more and more sophisticated language the simple delight he took in seeing the pigs at the farm when he was six. While working on *The Indelible Alison Bechdel*, I ran across An "Odd, Strange, and Curious Collection of Alison Bechdel's Works"—a cardboard-bound compilation I made of my best stories and drawings when I was twelve. The parallels are alarming—from the background details in the drawings to the use of marginal comments on the selected pieces.

Whether I've made stylistic progress since those days is open to debate, but like the pig boy, the spirit of my work (not to mention my editorial methodology) has remained consistent. Here's to animal husbandry.

Chapter one
Female Trouble

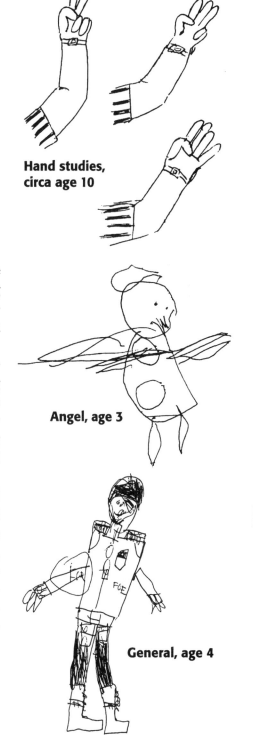

Hand studies, circa age 10

Angel, age 3

General, age 4

I'm always a little nonplussed when someone asks me when and/or why I started cartooning. Isn't cartooning an innate human behavior like eating, or whining? Doesn't everyone start drawing funny pictures as soon as they can clench a crayon?

I spent the better part of my childhood holed up in makeshift offices that I would construct around the house, drawing under a high-intensity lamp, refining my technique on reams and reams of typing paper. My life has changed remarkably little since those days, and I am rather smug about managing to make a living doing the same thing I've been doing since I was three years old.

Drawing people has always been my passion. As a child, I rarely bothered creating backgrounds for my figures because I was too eager to move on to my next subject. I drew hundreds of soldiers, cowboys, Indians, baseball players, executioners, boxers, chefs, explorers, policemen, firemen, musicians, scientists, lumberjacks, farmers, spies, mountain climbers, lifeguards, astronauts, accountants, disc jockeys, coal miners, businessmen, and bartenders, among numerous other central casting types.

In those days before affirmative action I didn't give much thought to the fact that none of these characters were female. But in retrospect, the glaring absence of women among my childhood drawings has made me think a lot.

I was a kid during the '60s. You didn't have to be a rocket scientist, or even a little lesbian, to see that women were getting a raw deal everywhere you looked. The combination of this everyday cultural misogyny, my naturally hypercritical personality, and the unusually androcentric dynamics of my family, made me quiveringly alive to every nuance of unequal treatment.

Cat-cowboy with horse, age 5

Excerpt from an early graphic novella, age 8. This was before I learned the secret of speech balloons: write the caption first, then draw the balloon.

Guy walking, age 7

Barbershop, age 11

Bad guys and loot, age 7

The world felt like a "Dennis the Menace" cartoon to me. Girls, even when they were good, were bad. Boys, even when they were bad, were good. And when girls were bad, if I may shift my frame of reference to "Peanuts," they were *really* bad.

My method of coping with this perverse moral order was to abdicate my girlhood. I didn't want to be associated with such a downtrodden people. I began carrying a pocket knife, begged to have my hair cut short, took up spitting. I had no illusion that I was a boy, though I liked being mistaken for one. But it was just as clear to me that I wasn't really a "girl."

Oh, I continued using the girls' bathroom and checking the female box on questionnaires. But in my head I occupied my own private Switzerland, where I spent the remainder of my childhood in splendid neutrality.

In a way, the men I drew weren't as much men as they were neutral, generic people. If I could have figured out how to draw women in a way that didn't preclude their peoplehood, I would have done it.

But kids don't learn to draw on a blank slate. They don't study the essence of a real tree in order to draw a tree; they draw it from a combination of memory, imagination, and convention. The way to draw a girl, I somehow absorbed, was to draw a regular person, then add certain signifiers: long hair, a skirt, high heels, huge curling eyelashes. I didn't look like that, and there was something instinctively offensive to me about overgeneralizing women merely as a way to differentiate them from "regular"–i.e. male–people.

I hadn't read *The Second Sex* yet–in fact, I hadn't learned to read–but it was clear to me that this treatment of "woman" as some sort of special case, as something other than a regular person, was a serious problem. All the comics, illustrations, and animated cartoons I grew up with reinforced this otherness one way or another. I've isolated four of the most common techniques they employed, all of which are still in use now, thirty years later.

Woman as Mutant

The female character is drawn as if she's a completely different species from the male. Witness the female cat's bizarre, human lips.

Woman as Drag Queen

The female is a male with accessories.

Woman as Fetish

Women's sexual features are emphasized and exaggerated. This is such a common practice that it's often invisible. I didn't really notice it until I saw my first cartoons by gay men and realized that if Dagwood were drawn in the same way Blondie is, this is what he'd look like.

All-Male Revue

Women are nonexistent except, perhaps, for one sacrificial victim. Children's literature is full of scenarios like this. *Winnie the Pooh, The Wind in the Willows, Peter Pan,* Hergé's "Tintin" comics. Entire universes where everyone is male except for the occasional mother or love interest.

Beard study, age 10

But my own propensity for an all-male cast can't be explained completely by this tidy feminist analysis. There was another force at work that I don't understand as clearly. Simply put, I was fascinated by masculinity. Some girls drew horses. I drew detailed studies of muscles, facial hair, football players, and the finer points of haberdashery.

Through my drawings, I entered an imaginary world of tough men. A recurrent motif was a big man kicking sand on a little man, à la Charles Atlas. I wanted to be that sandkicker. At night I would look at my protruding ribs in the mirror and fantasize about what would happen if I sent away for the weight-gain drinks advertised in the back of my comic books. Once I did respond to an ad that promised "The Secret to Superhuman Strength," but it turned out to be a disappointingly technical booklet about an obscure martial art.

age 11

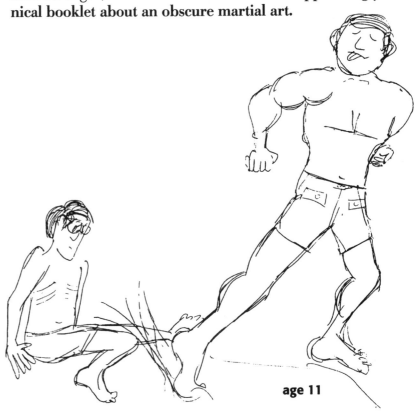

age 11

An even more disappointing booklet, however, was the one they passed out to all the girls in sixth grade. *Growing up and liking it* sounded like a threat to me. My Swiss passport was in jeopardy. They were trying to force me back into girldom, but I held out as long as I could, sustained by the cheerfully violent world of my drawings.

Growing up and liking it

age 13

Eventually my body betrayed me. My protruding ribs were replaced with protruding breasts. I hated how I looked.

There was no denying I was a girl now, but it was just as well because the pressure to conform was savage in my small, farm-country high school. I stopped carrying my defiantly androgynous bookbag and got a purse, started wearing makeup, went to the prom, associated with cheerleaders. My masquerade required herculean efforts of self-repression. After a long day of being a model teenage girl, I would come home and release my manic, pent-up energy through my fountain pen.

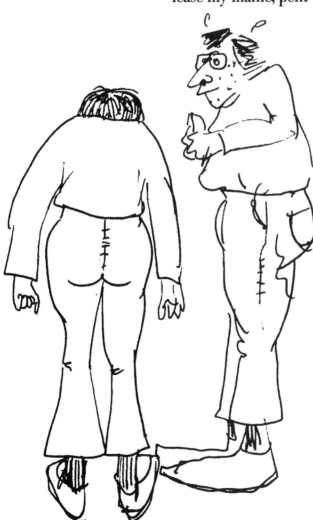

Self-hating self-portrait, rear and side views, age 15

I found this double life was unnecessary once I got to college. No one wore makeup or carried a purse or even shaved their legs there, and I was free to reconstruct my gender-neutral self. But the frenetic energy of my drawings continued unabated. Figures exploded with frustration or seethed inwardly. A cartoony religious imagery crept into my work, crucifixions and St. Sebastians, devils and angels. Everyone appeared to be in either agony or ecstasy.

Perhaps it's all too obvious that my gender wasn't the only thing in neutral. Sexually, I was a cipher. I didn't seem to mesh with anyone on that level. I tried to work up an attraction to a boy, which he listlessly returned for a while. And I had no idea that the feeling I had for various girls was genuine attraction. This oblivious state of affairs freed up my time tremendously, and for the first two years of my college career I was an assiduous student.

age 16

age 18

St. Sebastian, age 19

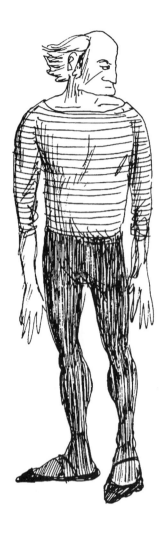

I dutifully cranked out projects for my art courses, but at night my sketchbooks bloomed with men. The central casting types had grown a tad more exotic. New motifs appeared. A more effeminate man started cropping up. The businessman, who had always been a stock character for me, grew playful, exuberant, and eventually airborne.

Then, just before my junior year, he began sprouting wings. It was clear to me that getting the wings was painful but ultimately a good thing.

23

That fall I finally realized I was a lesbian. It struck me then as increasingly odd that I was only drawing men when women were the ones who interested me.

I also began to acknowledge, now that I was a lesbian, that I must really be a *woman.* At least according to the dictionary. And if I was a woman, it followed that all the sexism and misogyny I saw in the world was directed at *me.* I became a big feminist after I came out, which was the reverse order from how most of my peers seemed to be going about things. I secretly prided myself on this, as well as on never having slept with boys, because it gave my until now haphazard life an aura of destiny and meaning. After years of neutrality it was intoxicating to be part of a group.

As I grew more and more politicized, it began to rankle that my sketchbooks were devoid of women. It wasn't simply that I chose not to draw women: I really couldn't draw them with anything like the fluency with which I drew men. I had no problem drawing women from life in my figure drawing classes. But life drawing was deliberate, an exercise in hand-eye coordination, a learned skill. It was a completely different activity from the almost involuntary drawing I did in my sketchbooks.

To draw a woman involved not just a change of subject matter but rewiring the circuitry that seemed to run directly from my subconscious to my pen. Because they originated in a more colonized region of my brain, my drawings of women came out graceless and stiff, and still looked a lot like men. My early attempts were so embarassing that I destroyed them.

Life drawing from a college class

Eventually I found that if I thought of the woman I was drawing as a lesbian, it was easier. There was more of a brain/pen connection than when I just drew a generic woman. My first, primitive lesbians were definitely on the butch side, and tended to have vestigial-looking two-dimensional breasts, but I was on my way.

I'd finished college by this point, and having been rejected by all the graduate art programs I applied to, was pursuing a string of menial publishing industry jobs in New York City. My drawings of lesbians were loosening up and becoming almost as free and cathartic as my drawings of men.

Early vestigial-breasted lesbian

Marianne, the first dyke to watch out for, 1982

One day, one of these women cropped up in the margin of a letter I was writing to a friend. I titled the drawing "Marianne, dissatisfied with the breakfast brew," and for some reason was moved to further label it "Dykes to Watch Out For, plate no. 27," as if it were just one in a series of illustrations of mildly demonic lesbians.

The concept of a series, although initially a joke, begged for continuation. I found myself drawing more and more "plates" in my sketchbooks over the next several months. The captions grew increasingly complex, and the drawings more finished and deliberate. Eventually I had a small sheaf of dykes to watch out for that I would whip out and display to acquaintances at the slightest provocation.

One friend encouraged me to submit some of the drawings to the collective of *Womanews*, the feminist monthly newspaper where we both volunteered. I did, and the first "Dykes To Watch Out For" was published in the July-August 1983 issue. People liked it, and I began doing a cartoon for every issue.

There was an incredibly positive and enthusiastic response to these early cartoons. At the time I took it rather coolly in stride, having suspected that I was a genius all along. But in retrospect it's clear that there was something else going on. The quality of the drawing and writing was wildly uneven—more often than not the cartoons weren't even funny—but lesbians were so desperate to see a reflection of their lives that it didn't seem to matter much.

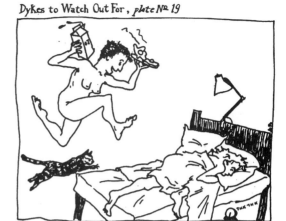

Dykes to Watch Out For, plate No. 19

Twyla is appalled to learn that Irene is a morning person.

"Madeleine gloats over the neat logic of her metaphor," 1983

First strip-format "Dykes To Watch Out For," 1984

First appearance of Mo and Lois, 1987

With so much encouragement, I continued drawing. And, slowly improving. After nine months of creating single-panel cartoons, it was getting harder and harder to come up with one-liners, so I switched to a strip format. Once I got the hang of drawing the same character more than once, I found it easier to create these longer cartoons. Each month the strip would have a different topic—dating, being mistaken for a man, literary lesbians to watch out for—and a fresh cast of characters.

After a year of doing strips exclusively for *Womanews*, I started sending them around to a few other papers. Some paid me, and some didn't. I cut back to a part-time job and made the rest of my living from freelance illustration gigs and my cartoons. Around this time I got a letter from Nancy Bereano, who was just founding Firebrand Books, and wanted to talk to me about publishing a collection of my cartoons. That first book came out in the fall of 1986.

With the momentum of the book under my belt, I took another creative leap. I started drawing the strip bi-weekly instead of monthly, and I introduced regular characters with an ongoing story line. Mo and Lois debuted in January 1987: the strip has been following the saga of life in their community ever since.

Over the years, I've pretty much stopped doing the free drawing that I used to fill sketchbooks with. After meeting a deadline, the last thing I want to do is pick up a pen again. But when I do occasionally sit down in front of a fresh, blank sheet of paper, or when I'm talking on the phone, or taking notes at a lecture, the drawings that cover my page are almost always of men. Hulking, willowy, muscular, mustachioed, bald, winged, naked, in dishabille, besuited—vibrating with energy.

It doesn't bother me anymore that they're not women. I've stopped worrying about their ideological import. The point is, they're still there, springing from whatever subconscious well they sprang from when I was three. I'm just glad it's not dry yet.

Chapter two
The Wonderful World of Me

Writing cartoons about my own life is a sort of guilty pleasure, a potent mix of self-indulgence and self-flagellation that no doubt has deep roots in my Catholic upbringing. And, in fact, there's something about autobiographical cartooning that's peculiarly conducive to confession.

Maybe it's the considerable degree of self-examination required to reduce yourself to a black-and-white cartoon. Or maybe, on the other hand, it's the critical distance created by stepping outside yourself enough to draw a picture of yourself that makes the medium so serviceable for plumbing inner depths.

Panel from "The Crush," my first autobiographical effort. Published in *Gay Comics* **#10, 1986, and reprinted in** *More Dykes To Watch Out For.*

BEING ALMOST PATHOLOGICALLY ROMANTIC, I'D SALVAGED QUITE AN ARRAY OF FLOTSAM AND JETSAM FROM THE SHIPWRECKS OF MY VARIOUS RELATIONSHIPS OVER THE YEARS.

SCAB FROM #3'S FOREHEAD (HISTORIC BIKE WRECK)

GROCERY LIST COMPOSED BY #6

BRAID FROM WHEN #4 CUT HER HAIR OFF

#2'S MERIT LIGHT BUTT

#1'S SOCK LINT

Panel from "Serial Monogamy,"
Dykes To Watch Out For: The Sequel

Drawing yourself lays bare the autobiographical premise— look at me!—and has the unexpected side effect of making a cartoon seem less, rather than more, self-conscious. Consequently, cartoonists get away with being obsessively self-absorbed in a way even memoir writers don't. In fact, autobiographical cartooning is a popular and growing field, most of whose practitioners are not content simply to navel-gaze, but must also collect the lint they find there. And on occasion are compelled to eat it. Lurid revelations about the author's hygiene, personality disorders, and sexual quirks are de rigeur. My own autobiographical cartoons aren't quite so morbid, but maybe I'll get braver as I age. I love working in this form, and keep trying to find a way to make time for it.

The challenge of autobiography is to transcend its inherent egocentrism enough that someone else will be interested. And if you don't succeed, it's no big deal. If your story strikes a reader as dull or conceited, it "may be read or not as anyone pleases," as Benjamin Franklin points out so helpfully at the beginning of *his* autobiography.

Of course, even the dullest autobiographical tale is still a "true story," to which a certain automatic level of interest accrues. I get asked constantly if the characters in "Dykes To Watch Out For" are actual people I know, if the things that happen in the strip are based on my life. I used to think these questions were incredibly naive, like something those people who believe soap opera characters are real would ask. But then I realized I often had the same questions myself about books I read. After hearing a story, the universal human response seems to be, "So, did any of that really happen?"

If "Dykes To Watch Out For" were about my real life, the strip would be phenomenally dull. And if all the stuff in the comic strip really happened to me, I wouldn't have time to sit around writing cartoons about it. But over the years I have managed to write a few stories about things that actually, really, truly happened to me, and here they are. Read them or not.

I drew this piece in 1989 for *Wimmen's Comix* #15. They were calling for comics in which the major character was a little girl. I was really intimidated by the prospect of writing about childhood and figured it was safer to stick with something that had actually happened than to make up a story. Still, I was almost paralyzed by trying not to be cute or condescending, and by trying to find a balance between my adult perspective and the immediacy of the childhood experience. Lynda Barry is such an expert at this, I thought it would help to read lots of her cartoons. But that only ended up intimidating me further.

After some struggle, I got the story down. It goes pretty well until the last panel, when the narration suddenly shifts. I had used an adult voice throughout the story, but the line"...you couldn't expect such a great mitt as this one for nothing" is a patronizing attempt at capturing the child's voice.

If I could rewrite this piece, I would explain less. I'd delete "I felt pretty weird" from the next-to-last panel, then change the last panel to read simply, "I figured that it must have been some sort of exchange."

It's the REAL LIFE LESBIAN ANIMAL ADVENTURE Series! 50¢

ONE SPRING, I WAS OUT JOGGING WITH MY LOVER AND OUR DOG, ETHEL.

THE FIELDS WERE FLOODED RIGHT UP TO THE EDGE OF THE ROAD WITH MELTING SNOW. I NOTICED A SMALL WHIRLPOOL AT ONE SPOT AND WENT TO INVESTIGATE. MY GIRLFRIEND KEPT RUNNING.

ETHEL WAS CURIOUS TOO, BUT THE BANK GAVE WAY AND SHE SLIPPED INTO THE DEEP WATER!

JUST AS I REACHED FOR HER COLLAR, SHE WENT UNDER!

WITHOUT THINKING, I JUMPED IN AFTER HER, ONLY TO SEE THE WHITE OF HER COAT **DISAPPEARING** THROUGH AN **UNDERWATER PIPE!**

THE FORCE OF THE ICY WATER PINNED ME AGAINST THE BANK, AND IN MY GRIEF AND SHOCK I COULD ONLY GRUNT INARTICULATELY TO MY LOVER.

UNNNH! ANNNH!

SHE QUICKLY YANKED ME OUT, THEN TURNED AND RAN ACROSS THE ROAD.

I FOLLOWED JUST IN TIME TO SEE ETHEL COME SHOOTING OUT THE OTHER END OF THE PIPE!

SHE PADDLED TO THE SIDE, COUGHED...

KACK

... AND SHOOK ...

...THEN JUST KEPT RUNNING AS IF NOTHING HAD HAPPENED!

WHAT A DOG!

I felt odd drawing my real girlfriend in this piece. We had broken up by the time I wrote it, and it seemed like I was stealing her story. In other pieces I've disguised lovers, but changing anything about this intimate drama would have felt like lying.

Gay Comics #19, 1993

In 1993, I was invited to create a special issue of new work for *Gay Comics*, an anthology comic book. After years of being constrained by the tiny panels of my biweekly comic strip, I was excited about having whole pages to fill up. I was also itching to write about my own tedious life instead of Mo's.

Drawing my coming out story seemed like a natural thing to do. It's one of the important stories of my life. It was hard to pare down the complexity of the experience into a cohesive narrative, and there are many, many things that by necessity were left out or simplified. Sometimes I regret having written this piece because it's had the effect of "freezing" the story for me. Now when someone asks me how I came out, I feel like I'm quoting myself.

This story takes place at Oberlin College in Ohio. I wasn't able to find any of the visual references I needed to draw the campus properly in time for my deadline, so I just faked it. I feel like this was an inexcusable professional lapse. I can't stand looking at these drawings knowing that they're not correct.

If the campus architecture is a little sketchy, at least I got my desk down accurately (bottom panel). This is thanks to a perverse habit I've always had of taking photographs of my work space in various living situations.

JADED ART MAJOR ATTITUDE

BUT THEN CAME THAT FATEFUL DAY IN NOVEMBER OF 1979. I WAS A JUNIOR IN COLLEGE.

I HAD JUST BEEN BROWSING AT THE CAMPUS BOOK-STORE, SOMETHING I DID A LOT OF IN THOSE DAYS.

Co-Op Bookstore

I WAS LONELY, A NEW TRANSFER STUDENT. BEING ENTIRELY ASEXUAL, APOLITICAL, AND ASOCIAL, I HADN'T MADE MANY FRIENDS YET.

WHEN I WASN'T IN CLASS OR AT THE BOOKSTORE, I WAS GETTING HIGH AND GOING TO MOVIES.

MY CINEMATIC EDUCATION WOULD HAVE BEEN EXCELLENT IF I COULD REMEMBER ANY OF IT.

THE DRUGS, THE ENDLESS MOVIEGOING, THE HOURS OF BROWSING THROUGH BOOKS... I WAS TRYING DESPERATELY TO DISTRACT MYSELF FROM A TRUTH THAT WAS SLOWLY BUT SURELY STRUGGLING TO THE SURFACE OF MY SOLITARY, SEX-STARVED SOUL.

ONE OF THE BOOKS I CHANCED TO FLIP THROUGH THAT PARTICULAR GRAY AFTERNOON WAS "ABOUT HOMOSEXUALS," AS I LATER NOTED IN MY JOURNAL.

VARIOUS PEOPLE WERE INTERVIEWED ABOUT HOW THEY HAD COME TO REALIZE THEY WERE GAY, AND WHAT THEIR LIVES WERE LIKE.

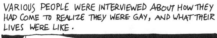

I READ FOR A WHILE, THEN AT MY USUAL TIME I LEFT THE BOOKSTORE AND HEADED BACK TO MY DORM.

IN A CRUEL TWIST OF FATE, I FOUND MYSELF FENDING OFF **NERDBOYS** WHILE MY WILDLY POPULAR AND HIP HETEROSEXUAL ROOMMATE HAD DISCOVERED **REAL LIVE LESBIANS!**

SHE SEEMED TO HAVE ACCESS TO A WORLD I DIDN'T EVEN KNOW EXISTED... AND SHE SPOKE SO CARELESSLY OF MY DEEPEST HOPES AND FEARS!

DESPAIR BECKONED... WHAT WAS "PRO-CHOICE?" IT SOUNDED LIKE SOME **FRINGE** POLITICAL GROUP! AND MEETINGS AT THE **WOMEN'S CENTER?** THIS STUFF WAS WAY OUT OF MY LEAGUE!

BUT I PERSEVERED, IN MY OWN QUIET WAY. THE BOOKSTORE YIELDED ANOTHER HELPFUL VOLUME.

TOO NERVOUS TO READ SOMETHING SO BLATANT IN PUBLIC, I **BOUGHT** IT.

PULSE WELL ABOVE MAXIMUM RECOMMENDED RATE.

I READ THE WHOLE BOOK VORACIOUSLY. IT WAS VERY ENCOURAGING. WHEN I WAS DONE, I TORE THE COVER OFF, STUFFED THE REST OF IT IN A BROWN PAPER BAG, AND HID IT UNDER MY MATTRESS.

NEXT, I TOOK TO READING THE LESBIAN CHAPTER OF MY ROOMMATE'S **HITE REPORT** WHILE SHE WAS OUT.

HI!

HI... UH... I WAS JUST LOOKING FOR YOUR DICTIONARY.

ONE THING LED TO ANOTHER, AND BEFORE THE SEMESTER WAS OVER I HAD DEVOURED **DESERT OF THE HEART, RUBYFRUIT JUNGLE,** AND **THE WELL OF LONELINESS.**

WHERE'S TH' SEXY PARTS?

FLIP

THE WELL OF LONELINESS RADCLYFFE HALL

CHRISTMAS BREAK WAS INTERMINABLE. MY PARENTS FAILED TO NOTICE THAT I HAD BECOME A THREAT TO THE NUCLEAR FAMILY.

A CHENILLE ROBE! THANKS.

AT LAST I WAS BACK AT SCHOOL. I WAS ENROLLED IN AN INTENSIVE COURSE ON JAMES JOYCE'S **ULYSSES.** I SKIMMED IT...

768 PAGES...

... MY FULL ACADEMIC PASSION WAS RESERVED FOR A **DIFFERENT** ODYSSEY... THE QUEST FOR MY **PEOPLE**.

WHAT A LITTLE BOOKWORM! I HAD AN INSATIABLE HUNGER FOR KNOWLEDGE.

YEAH, AMONG OTHER THINGS. DON'T FORGET TO MENTION THE LONG HOURS YOU SPENT **WHACKING OFF**.

HUMP HUMP

This story is the one thing I've done that I haven't shown my mom—because of the masturbation scene in panel 3. I've never had any qualms about her seeing all the explicit fictional sex I've drawn in my books, but I can't help feeling squeamish about this discreet real-life example. Hiding the *Gay Comics* issue from her was easy, but I have a feeling she's probably going to notice that I published this book.

WELL, YES... OF COURSE THERE WAS A DEGREE OF SEXUAL FRUSTRATION INVOLVED.

KOFF.

AFTER ALL, I STILL HADN'T MET ANY LESBIANS. AND IF I **DID**, WOULD THEY FIND ME AS ATTRACTIVE AS THE **NERDBOYS** SEEMED TO?

I WAS DYING TO HAVE SEX WITH A WOMAN. DYING.

I'M DYING.

ALSO SWIPED FROM ROOMMATE

I PRAYED FOR A KINDLY, EXPERIENCED LESBIAN TO COME RESCUE ME FROM MY LONELY AGONIES.

YES?

NOK NOK

BUT ALL I GOT WAS ANOTHER BOY.

HI. I MET YOU AT THE LIBRARY, REMEMBER? CARE TO SMOKE A STOGIE?

WHY NOT?

THIS ONE WAS DIFFERENT, THOUGH. WE REALLY HIT IT OFF AND ENDED UP TALKING ALL NIGHT IN HIS ROOM.

YOU DRAW? COULD I SEE YOUR SKETCHBOOKS SOMETIME?

YEAH, SURE.

CARTIER BRESSON

The best material happens when my story collides with someone else's, but it's like a joint bank account: it doesn't seem right to make a withdrawal without letting the other person know. I had been out of touch with the guy in this scene for years and didn't bother tracking him down to see how he felt about appearing in my comic book.

INSTEAD OF FEELING REPULSED WHEN HE MADE HIS MOVE AT 4 A.M., I JUST FELT SAD.

WELL, I FEEL LIKE IT'S ABOUT TIME TO LIGHT A CANDLE AND LIE DOWN.

OH.

I RETURNED, NUN-LIKE, TO MY CELL.

WELL, I'D BETTER BE GOING THEN. I HAD A LOVELY EVENING.

HE SHOWED UP AT MY DOOR THE NEXT DAY AT NOON.

I COULDN'T SLEEP. I'VE BEEN WALKING ALL OVER... I WROTE YOU THIS POEM.

IT WASN'T HALF-BAD, EITHER.

WE HAD A LONG, HALTING DISCUSSION ABOUT WHY I'D LEFT HIS ROOM SO ABRUPTLY. FINALLY, HE SAID SOMETHING SO REMARKABLE THAT I ANSWERED WITHOUT THINKING.

...I DON'T UNDERSTAND. I MEAN, IF YOU WERE MORE ATTRACTED TO WOMEN...

THAT'S EXACTLY IT!

IT WAS AS IF A THUNDERBOLT HAD SPLIT THE AIR! MY SECRET WAS REVEALED! I HAD COME OUT TO ANOTHER PERSON!

INTOXICATED WITH RELIEF, I POURED MY HEART AND SOUL OUT TO THAT UNFORTUNATE YOUNG MAN. HE WAS QUITE DECENT ABOUT IT.

FROM EARLIEST CHILDHOOD, I KNEW I WAS DIFFERENT FROM OTHER GIRLS...

BUT AFTERWARDS, I PANICKED.

WHAT HAVE I DONE?! WHAT HAS POSSESSED ME?! YOU CAN'T JUST GO AROUND TELLING PEOPLE YOU'RE A LESBIAN UNLESS YOU KNOW YOU ARE ONE! DO I ACTUALLY THINK I HAVE THE NERVE TO BE A LESBIAN?!! FUCK! FUCKING SHIT! I DON'T EVEN KNOW ANY WOMEN! WHAT MAKES ME THINK I'M ATTRACTED TO THEM?!

I WENT BACK TO THE GAY UNION DURING OFFICE HOURS. THEY HAD A TREASURE TROVE OF MAGAZINES AND BOOKS I HADN'T SEEN BEFORE.

IT'S ALL REALLY A MESS. I HOPE YOU CAN FIND WHAT YOU WANT.

Y'KNOW, I COULD ORGANIZE IT FOR YOU!

BUSY

R.F.D.

SINISTER WISDOM

CHRISTOPHER STREET

LESBIAN CONNECTION

AND THUS I BECAME THE OFFICE LIBRARIAN.

NEXT WEEK, I WENT OUT AFTER THE MEETING WITH THE "UNION" CROWD. I WAS A LITTLE NERVOUS ABOUT BEING SEEN IN PUBLIC WITH THEM.

DID I TELL YOU I THINK MY ECON. PROF. IS A DYKE?

BEN'S DRAG NAME IS MARY, AND I'M ESMERALDA.

3.2

"DYKE?" DRAG NAMES? THIS ALL SEEMS RATHER... UNHEALTHY!

THEY WERE EAGER TO INSTRUCT A NOVICE, BUT I COULDN'T REALLY RELATE TO THEM. I WAS PLAGUED WITH DOUBT.

YOU HAFTA LISTEN TO THIS ALBUM! IT'S SO INCREDIBLE. IT'S **OUR MUSIC!**

WHEN YOU'RE GIVING DIRECTIONS, NEVER SAY "STRAIGHT," ALWAYS SAY "GAYLY FORWARD."

LESBIAN **MUSIC?**

CHANGER AND THE CHANGED

THESE PEOPLE ARE **WEIRD.** MAYBE I'M NOT A HOMO AFTER ALL.

I KEPT GOING TO MEETINGS, THOUGH, AND GRADUALLY WE HIT ON SOME COMMON BONDS.

I HAD A **BAAD** CRUSH ON JULIE ANDREWS IN "THE SOUND OF MUSIC" WHEN I WAS FIVE.

ME TOO!

SLOWLY, I GAINED CONFIDENCE. I CAME OUT TO MY ROOMMATE.

OH, HOW COOL! CAN I TELL MY FRIENDS?

I DISCOVERED THE EXHILAR-ATION OF SPEAKING OUT AGAINST PREJUDICE.

HAVE YOU SEEN THAT CREEPY LESBIAN GRAFFITI IN THE BATH-ROOM? EW!

UH... WELL... I'M A... A LESBIAN, AND I SORT OF **LIKE** SEEING IT.

I DISCOVERED ALCOHOL.

GAY DANCE TONIGHT

 BUT I STILL HADN'T DISCOVERED **SEX**. THAT FINAL FRONTIER LOOMED AHEAD, TAUNTING ME, MOCKING MY PRIM, CEREBRAL PROGRESS THUS FAR.

FINALLY, AFTER A NIGHT OF DRUNKEN REVELRY, I BROUGHT TWO OF MY NEW FRIENDS BACK TO MY ROOM TO GET HIGH. I REMEMBER THE PIPE I RIGGED UP OUT OF AN EMPTY TOILET PAPER TUBE, BUT I DON'T REMEMBER WHAT WE TALKED ABOUT.

I DON'T REMEMBER BECKY LEAVING, BUT I DO REMEMBER THAT JOAN STAYED.

MIND IF I CRASH HERE? IT'S SO LATE.

I TURNED OFF THE LIGHT. WE REMOVED OUR JEANS AND GOT INTO MY SINGLE BED. STILL IN MY BRA AND WOOL SWEATER, I WAS PROFOUNDLY UNCOMFORTABLE.

AS WE LAY THERE, I BEGAN TO **SHIVER** UNCONTROLLABLY.

JEEZ, THIS IS WEIRD. MUST BE THAT GRAIN ALCOHOL..

THE WHOLE BED BEGAN TO SHAKE, BANGING AGAINST THE WALL.

WHAT'S WRONG?

CHATTER

THUMPA THUMP!

JOAN TRIED TO SOOTHE ME, BUT WHEREVER SHE TOUCHED ME, I WAS UNBEARABLY **TICKLISH**.

WHA HA HA!

EVENTUALLY, I RELAXED A BIT AND WE KISSED.

 45

the POWER of PRAYER

UNTIL THE SPRING OF SECOND GRADE, I WAS A CAREFREE, GODLESS CHILD. THE WORLD WAS MY OYSTER.

© 1993 BY ALISON BECHDEL

DID YOU SAY YOUR PRAYER?

I'M BUSY! CAN'T I SKIP A NIGHT?

THEN ONE DAY AT SCHOOL, THE TEACHER DIVIDED OUR CLASS BY SEX.

I WANT ALL THE BOYS TO GO QUIETLY WITH MR. WILLIS TO THE ART ROOM. QUIETLY!

GIRLS, YOU'RE COMING WITH ME.

OH GOODY!

RRRM! RRRM!

NOT EVEN MY WORST SUSPICIONS PREPARED ME FOR WHAT WAS TO FOLLOW.

OKAY, GIRLS! LET'S ALL TAKE OFF OUR SHOES AND PUT THEM NEATLY AGAINST THE WALL. MISS MOODLER IS OUR NEW **MODERN DANCE TEACHER**.

GULP

POP!
HISSS
CRACKLE

FOLLOW ME IN A CIRCLE, GIRLS! HOW DOES THIS MUSIC MAKE YOU FEEL? SHOW IT IN HOW YOU MOVE! SENSE THE RHYTHM.

HORRORSTRUCK, I REALIZED I HAD NO CHOICE BUT TO COMPLY WITH THEIR DEMENTED SCHEME.

HURRY UP, ALISON.

Gay Comics #19, 1993

"The Power of Prayer" was my second attempt at recounting an event from my childhood. I used the same technique I did in "The Mitt"—narrating the story with my adult voice—but this time I managed to keep it consistent.

I made a field trip to a local elementary school to do visual research for this piece. I didn't end up using most of it, but it never hurts to be overprepared. The radiator on the wall of the stairwell in the third panel is a great detail that I wouldn't have remembered about my own school if I hadn't seen it in the one I visited.

I WENT THROUGH THE MOTIONS IN ORDER TO AVOID BEING SINGLED OUT FOR SOME EVEN **WORSE** FATE.

BACK IN THE CLASSROOM, I THOUGHT MY HUMILIATION WAS OVER... BUT I WAS WRONG.

ALL THAT WEEK, I ENDURED THIS ASSAULT ON MY DIGNITY AND SELF-DETERMINATION.

BUT FINALLY THEY WENT TOO FAR. ONE DAY WE WERE GIVEN NOTES TO TAKE HOME.

FRIGHTENED, I CONCOCTED A SHORT-RANGE SOLUTION TO MY PLIGHT.

I WENT STRAIGHT TO MY ROOM AFTER SCHOOL AND CHANGED FROM MY GIRL COSTUME INTO MY REGULAR CLOTHES.

AFTER POCKETING THE TEACHER'S NOTE, I PICKED UP A TROWEL FROM THE GARAGE AND SET OFF FOR THE WOODS.

AT THE ABANDONED RAILROAD TRACKS, I STOPPED AND DUG A DEEP HOLE...

TORE THE NOTE INTO AS MANY PIECES AS I POSSIBLY COULD...

...AND BURIED THEM.

I WAS GIDDY WITH RELIEF.

THE NEXT DAY, HOWEVER, I HAD A BAD SCARE.

ALISON, ARE YOU LEARNING A DANCE IN SCHOOL?

SOMEONE'S MOTHER MUST HAVE SPILLED THE BEANS.

I PLAYED IT COOL, AND SHE DIDN'T SUSPECT A THING.

UM...NO.

OH.

CLINKETY CLACK!

BUT THE DAY OF THE GYM SHOW WAS FAST ENCROACHING. DESPERATE NOW, I HOPED FOR A MIRACLE.

ON SATURDAY, I ATTENDED MY REGULAR WEEKLY CHURCH SCHOOL CLASS. I HAD NEVER PAID MUCH ATTENTION BEFORE. IT ALL SEEMED SO ABSTRACT.

WHAT IF A BABY DIES BEFORE IT'S BAPTIZED?

WELL, TOMMY, SINCE THE BABY HAS ORIGINAL SIN, IT WILL **BURN** IN **HELL**.

49

I depend a lot on my girlfriend's advice about my work. When I showed her this finished piece, she thought the ending was too "soft," that I hadn't really resolved the story completely. Normally when we disagree about my work, one of us is able to make a sufficient case to convince the other. But this time neither of us would back down, even after a strangely prolonged and heated debate. Since it was my story, I had the last word. But I've always had an irksome suspicion that maybe she was right.

BUT THAT MORNING, CATHOLIC DOCTRINE FELL INTO PLACE FOR ME.

> NOW, WHAT MUST WE DO TO GO TO HEAVEN?

> GET BAPTIZED AND SAY OUR **PRAYERS!**

THE NIGHT BEFORE THE GYM SHOW, I SAT UP IN BED SAYING A HUNDRED "OUR FATHERS."

> ...ANDELIVERUSFROMEVILAMENOUR FATHERWHOARTINHEAVENHALLOWEDBE...

I TICKED THEM OFF ON THE BACK OF A COMIC BOOK.

AND I AWOKE THE NEXT DAY WITH DIVINE INSPIRATION.

> I DON'T FEEL SO GOOD. MY STOMACH HURTS.

MIRACULOUSLY, IT WORKED.

> WHAT'S WRONG WITH YOU ANYWAY?

THE SITTER

> YOO HOO! MR. GREEN-JEANS!

> EARACHE.

AND EVEN MORE MIRACULOUSLY, WHEN MY MOTHER RETURNED FROM TAKING MY BROTHERS TO THE GYM SHOW THAT NIGHT, SHE DIDN'T MENTION MY CLASSMATES' LITTLE PERFORMANCE.

> HOW ARE YOU FEELING?

> BETTER, I THINK.

YES, I HAD BEEN DELIVERED FROM THE SCARF DANCE. BUT SOMEHOW I COULDN'T RECAPTURE MY FORMER CAREFREE ABANDON.

AFTER ALL, GOD ONLY KNEW WHAT FURTHER EVILS THIS LIFE HELD IN STORE.

JUST TO BE ON THE SAFE SIDE, I SAID ANOTHER HUNDRED PRAYERS BEFORE I LAY DOWN AND SLEPT.

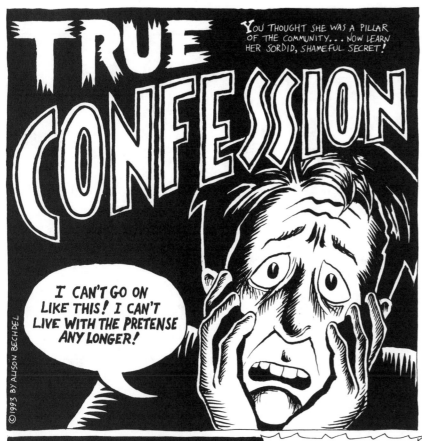

Gay Comics #19, 1993

"True Confession" is a cartoon about being a cartoonist. To add yet another level of self-reflexivity by commenting on it any further seems excessive, so I'll stop right here.

The girlfriend in panels 2 and 3 has been disguised. I tried really hard (well, sort of) not to trash her here for wanting to stay in the closet, but it was very traumatic for me to go along with her pretense. Afterward, it seemed like the least I could do was confess publicly.

This piece happened without a lot of suffering and rewriting. It just works. It manages to explain a highly complex and somewhat painful experience in seven panels, while at the same time being fairly funny. If only it were always this easy.

my life as a boy

ONE BLOSSOM-SCENTED SPRING EVENING DURING MY EARLY TWENTIES, I WAS OUT FOR A WALK WITH MY GIRLFRIEND.

SHE HAD JUST HITCHIKED HER WAY BACK TO NEW YORK FROM NICARAGUA, AND I WAS IN TRAINING FOR MY BLACK BELT EXAM.

IT WAS A BUTCH-BUTCH SORT OF RELATIONSHIP. WE WRESTLED A LOT, AND DIDN'T SAY WE LOVED EACH OTHER UNTIL OUR FIRST ANNIVERSARY.

OW! MY ARM!

FAKER!

SO IT WAS THAT NEITHER OF US MISSED A BEAT WHEN A STRANGE MAN CALLED TO US FROM HIS STOOP.

HEY, YOU FELLAS WANNA MAKE FIVE BUCKS? I NEED TO GET THIS DESK UP TO THE THIRD FLOOR.

SURE.

OKAY.

AT CLOSE RANGE, IT WAS CLEAR THAT WE WERE TWO ADULT WOMEN, BUT HE WAS TOO FLUSTERED TO RETRACT HIS PROPOSAL.

YOU OKAY?

YEAH. JUST GO SLOW.

UH...HERE YOU GO. THANKS A LOT.

ANY TIME.

WE USED THE MONEY TO BUY ICE CREAM.

FRENCH VANILLA
CHOC CHOC CHIP
BOYSENBERRY
MOCHA CHIP

Häagen

I FELT CURIOUSLY LIGHT AND INVINCIBLE AS WE WALKED HOME IN THE BALMY MAY DUSK.

My ex turned out not to mind the story I'd done about her dog going through the pipe, so I went ahead and told another tale from our relationship. This story takes place in Park Slope, Brooklyn, which has a very distinctive architectural look. I couldn't find any photos to work from at the library and had to improvise from the buildings in some Charles Addams cartoons.

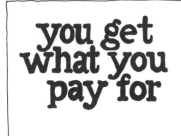

you get what you pay for

A NOTHER TRENCHANT IF SLIGHTLY EMBROIDERED TALE FROM THE LIFE OF THE ARTIST.

ONE DAY I WENT INTO A SANDWICH SHOP WITH A FRIEND TO GET LUNCH.

MY FRIEND GAVE HER ORDER TO ONE OF THE YOUNG STRAIGHT GIRLS BEHIND THE COUNTER. I GAVE MINE TO THE OTHER ONE.

UH... COULD I GET HAM ON WHOLE WHEAT WITH MAYO, TOMATO, ONION, AND LETTUCE?

I'D LIKE HUMMUS ON PUMPERNICKEL WITH SPROUTS AND PICKLES.

EVERYTHING WAS GOING SMOOTHLY...

UNTIL THE STRAIGHT GIRLS **CONFUSED** US FOR ONE ANOTHER.

MAYO, TOMATO, ONION, AND LETTUCE, RIGHT?

UH...NO. HUMMUS, SPROUTS, AND PICKLES.

THE MIX-UP WOULD HAVE BEEN NIPPED IN THE BUD HAD WE ONLY REALIZED THAT WE WERE CONFUSING **THEM** FOR ONE ANOTHER TOO, BUT WE DIDN'T.

YOU WANTED HUMMUS AND SPROUTS ON THIS, RIGHT?

NO, JUST MAYO, TOMATO, ONION, AND LETTUCE.

WHAT ARE THEY **TEACHING** THEM IN SANDWICH SCHOOL THESE DAYS?

AFTER COMPLETING OUR TRANSACTIONS,...

THANKS! YOU TWO LOOK SO ALIKE! ARE YOU SISTERS?

TYPICAL.

WE LEFT, NOT A LITTLE SELF-RIGHTEOUSLY.

SISTERS! SHEESH! STUPID HETS THINK WE ALL LOOK ALIKE!

PINHEADS! THEY JUST DON'T **LOOK.**

IT WASN'T UNTIL WE OPENED OUR SANDWICHES THAT OUR OWN PINHEADEDNESS BECAME APPARENT.

HEY, THIS IS JUST A BUNCH OF VEGETABLES!

HUMMUS AND **HAM?** WHAT TH'?

Trying to retell this ironic "they all look alike" incident just about gave me a brain hemorrhage. I think it would work a lot better if I just deleted all the explanatory narration and left the dialogue to stand on its own.

I drew this piece for *Strange Looking Exile, The Comix Zine for Queer Dudes and Babes.* Robert Kirby, who also draws the strip "Curbside," edited five issues of this excellent comics anthology. Working for a zine was really freeing. I'd been getting used to a relatively large audience seeing my comic strips and books, and was unconsciously taking fewer and fewer risks in my work in order to keep everyone happy.

"Michigan Hell" is another self-absorbed cartoon about the cartoonist's lot. This story seems tame to me now, but at the time it was thrilling to confess how much I hated such an august (in both senses of the word) institution as the Michigan Womyn's Music Festival.

Strange Looking Exile, 1993

Panel 1: SINCE I WAS WORKING 18 HOURS A DAY, I DIDN'T GO TO ANY OF THE CONCERTS OR WORKSHOPS. I EVEN MISSED THE MOST SPECTACULAR METEOR SHOWERS IN YEARS.

WOO-OOO! ♪ WHISTLE ♪ gasp! CLAP CLAP YAY! CLAP

BUNCH OF SLACKERS!

SEVERAL THOUSAND LESBIANS WATCHING FALLING STARS

Panel 2: MY MOOD WAS NOT IMPROVED BY THE FACT THAT SALES WERE SLOW.

D'YOU HAVE ANY OF THOSE SHIRTS?

BOM BOM BUDDA BOM

T-SHIRTS $12 MUGS $10

Watch For Junk

Panel 3: A SENSE OF CLAUSTROPHOBIA BEGAN TO CREEP OVER ME. AT FIRST I THOUGHT IT WAS JUST MY CLAMMY SLEEPING BAG...

BA DUM BA DUM BIDDA BOM

AAAUGH!

TAM PAX

Panel 4: BUT SOON I WAS FEELING IT EVEN OUTSIDE, IN THE MIDDLE OF AN OPEN MEADOW.

I HAVE TA GET OUT OF HERE!

BOM BA DUMA DUM BIDDA BOM DUM

Panel 5: SATURDAY NIGHT, THERE SEEMED TO BE EVEN MORE NOISE THAN USUAL. AFTER DRAWING UNTIL MY HAND CRAMPED UP, I WENT TO INVESTIGATE.

Panel 6: IT WAS A HUGE AL FRESCO DANCE PARTY. A SEA OF SWEATY, ECSTATIC WOMEN PULSATED UNDER THE STARS TO A DRIVING, ANCIENT BEAT.

♪♫ FREE YOUR MIND! THE REST WILL FOL-LOW ♪♫

GREAT. HOW'M I SUPPOSED TO SLEEP WITH ALL THIS RACKET?

Panel 7: NEXT DAY, THE FESTIVAL ENDED. AT 7 P.M., I PACKED UP MY BOOTH, BUT WE WEREN'T ALLOWED TO BRING OUR CARS IN TO LOAD OUR STUFF UNTIL MONDAY MORNING.

I'M SO BUMMED! CAN YOU BELIEVE WE HAVE TO LEAVE TOMORROW?

SEIKO 12.37.06

CHEAP COFFEE MUGS

Dykes to Watch

Panel 8: I COULDN'T STAND IT. WITH A BURST OF FRANTIC, DESPERATE ENERGY, I HAULED ALL MY BOXES AND GEAR TWO MILES IN A CART, IN THE DARK AND RAIN, TO MY CAR.

HILL!

I PROMISED THESE WOMEN MY FIRSTBORN CHILD.

FLAT TIRE

SQUEAL

I WAS OFF THE LAND BY 11 P.M.

Panel 9: A HUNDRED MILES AWAY, I SPENT THE HAPPIEST NIGHT OF MY LIFE.

4 WALLS, CEILING & DOOR

AIR CONDITIONER

Best Western

CABLE

CLEAN DRY

AH, WILDERNESS.

The End.

Chapter three
Character Development

Adventures in Monogamy

For the first couple of years, "Dykes To Watch Out For" had no recurrent characters or ongoing narrative. Creating that kind of a virtual world was a daunting prospect at a time when I could barely draw the same character recognizably from panel to panel. It seemed easier to invent a new scenario with a disposable cast each month. Sort of like the way it was easier to find a new girlfriend when things got too intimate with the one I already had.

I knew I wanted steady characters eventually, but I just wasn't ready to commit. Then, in 1987, several factors converged to force my hand. One was the burst of confidence that came with getting my first book published. The second was reading Howard Cruse's comic strip "Wendel" in the *Advocate*. "Wendel" was an ongoing strip about a goofy gay man, his lover Ollie, their co-workers, friends, and relations. I got wrapped up in their saga, and started to think about the storytelling possibilities a regular cast of my own would provide.

The third and perhaps deciding factor was that I was running out of subject matter. In my strips with disposable characters, I'd covered dating, breaking up, butch and femme, jocks, and music festivals, along with a few other stock, obligatory topics. At the time it seemed like I'd pretty much exhausted the lesbian gamut.

Yet even with all these forces at work, I gave surprisingly little thought to the actual introduction of Mo in 1987. If I were to undertake a new strip now, I'd have to create complex character histories, plot trajectories, and street maps before I even thought about the first episode. But back then my only notes before plunging in were, "A heroine. Real anxious & anal-retentive. Monica, "Mo" for short." Following the prescription to write what one knows, I made Mo like me: a young, white, middle-class, marginally employed lesbian-feminist. I tried to disguise her from looking too much like me by giving her glasses and longer hair. My success in this effort can be judged by how loudly people laugh when I tell them that.

Actually, all my characters are based on me. Mo is my guilt-ridden, liberal superego. Lois represents my secret desire to be one of the cool girls. Clarice is my driven, ambitious, workaholic side; Toni the flip domestic side. Sparrow is the part of me that wonders if maybe my chakras are blocked, and Ginger the part of me that alternates between thinking I'm a genius and thinking I'm an utter fraud, all the while procrastinating hopelessly.

I think of "Dykes To Watch Out For" as half op-ed column and half endless, serialized Victorian novel. Discussing current events and reflecting trends is as important to me as rendering the characters' lives in a believable, psychologically accurate way. Sometimes these two efforts complement one another—Clarice and Toni had a baby for personal reasons, but their situation provides

Prototype for the character of Lois. In the final version, she lost the tail.

lots of great tie-ins to topical issues like second-parent adoption and gay marriage. And sometimes one will predominate and obscure the other. For example, I decided to reveal that Lois was taking anti-depressants because it's something a lot of people are doing, but it's been a struggle to retrofit that fact with her apparently happy-go-lucky nature.

I love it when reviewers mention the novelistic qualities of "DTWOF," but character development, though integral to a novel, is somewhat antithetical to the task of writing a comic strip. While a novel might be about love, loss, and redemption, a comic strip is about running into your date naked at the Y, breaking off with her because she's still seeing her not-quite-ex, then immediately falling for the next inappropriate love interest who happens along. A comic strip, like life, is a novel that never seems to get anywhere.

But it's precisely this getting nowhere that's part of the appeal. Comic strips are an exaltation of the commonplace, the routine, the everyday. Recognizable characters and familiar scenarios are what make a strip endure. Occasionally I wonder if maybe Mo should outgrow her whining, impotent, judgmental nebbishness. But then I think if she were a perfectly self-actualized pillar of society, I wouldn't be writing the same comic strip anymore. I compromise by having her go through small, glacially paced transitions—enough to keep her from being too tiresome, but not enough to change her winsome, irritating essence.

This catch-22—having to introduce sufficient change to continue engaging readers, but not so much that it alienates them—makes writing an ongoing strip tricky. It's an increasing challenge to keep the strip fresh and relevant without altering anything substantive. For example, my characters Sparrow, Ginger, and Lois have been living together in a collective household for the past twelve years. As I write this, I'm trying to decide whether to break them up and have them go their separate ways. Part of me wants them to stay together because

CUNNING LINGUISTS

It's always a bit of a shock to see my characters speaking other languages. Here are a few translations people have done—some pirated, and some officially sanctioned.

Czech

Italian

63

French

German

Japanese

it's how they've always been and I like the way they work as a team. But part of me wants to split them up because the real-life likelihood of three lesbians who aren't involved with each other remaining at the same address that long is about one in a septillion.

When my characters were still new, I would assign them traits and predilections with abandon. I could make them be anything I wanted. But the longer I write about them, the more their personalities necessarily get pinned down and delineated, and the more their options diminish. Lois will never become a Buddhist nun, Sparrow will never transition into a man, Mo will never run for office, and that's all there is to it.

Though I occasionally feel trapped by this continually narrowing scope, most of the time I thrive on the creative challenge it presents. It's like realizing your lover is no longer the hazy, potentially perfect specimen you first met, but an all-too-distinct figure with her own damn way of doing things. The range of possibility that you once imagined with her has decreased, but the depth of possibility has hopefully expanded. Maybe you'll never scale Mt. Kilimanjaro together, but what's that to the thrill of finishing one another's sentences? As my characters have gotten better drawn, both literally and figuratively, I've been able to tell stories that are increasingly nuanced and less…well, black-and-white.

I'm glad I finally settled down with my harem of characters, and I look forward to exploring their cartoon psyches in ever-enlarging detail for years to come. Sometimes I'm a little haunted by the fates of strips like "Calvin and Hobbes," "Bloom County," and "The Far Side," whose creators got burnt out and nobly decided to quit before they lost their edge. I'd like to grow old with Mo and the other dykes, but if things ever stop working, I hope I'll have the sense to put down my pen before a member of the relationship charges mental cruelty.

Dramatis Personae

Mo is the nucleus of the strip for me. She embodies all the values that I assumed were part of being a lesbian when I came out. She's basically an antiracist, anticlassist, anti-big business, anticonsumerist feminist socialist. When I first started writing the strip, it often focused on Mo's struggle to live a socially responsible life in this country, and her frustration with her own inevitable complicity in the system. Lately my focus has shifted more to her frustration with her less-than-revolutionary friends, who do everything from ingest Prozac and meat, to pursue recognition from the State for their parental status. She has an especially intimate and thorny relationship with Clarice. Not only do they have very different activist strategies—Mo from outside and Clarice from inside the system—but they were each others' first lovers back in college.

Mo

Lois was introduced as the obligatory debonaire foil to the repressed and nerdlike Mo. I originally envisioned her as a devout nonmonogamist, but although we've seen her with plenty of lovers over the years, they've tended to be one at a time. It's been on my to-do list for years now to show her successfully juggling multiple relationships. She's been kind of a one-dimensional sex-positive poster girl, and I'm trying to flesh her out a bit more. So to speak. As an employee at Madwimmin Books, Lois has helped keep the store solvent by introducing a line of sex toys. But she's feeling a little left in the dust as her housemates Ginger and Sparrow get more and more focused on their careers.

Lois

Clarice is the father figure of the strip. As Toni, her very long-term partner says, "I love a butch in a skirt." Clarice struggles constantly to balance her career with her family, but more often than not career wins out. Right now she's an attor-

Clarice

Toni

Raffi

Ginger

ney for the Environmental Justice Fund, where she sues corporations like Union Carbuncle for dumping their hazardous waste disproportionately in poor neighborhoods. For a long time she was reluctant to become a parent. But she's so devoted to Raffi that she finds herself compromising her deepest values for his sake, like subjecting herself to court-ordered visits from a social worker to win second-parent adoption, and possibly even moving to a "better" neighborhood.

I have the maternal instinct of a doorknob, so Toni has always been a bit of an enigma to me. Being a mother is her top priority, and she quit her job as a C.P.A. to stay home with Raffi for a couple of years. Actually, it turned out to be more like four years, but that was mostly because I got distracted with other storylines and forgot to send her back to work. We rarely see the other characters' parents, but Toni's folks have been the focus of several strips. They had a hard time after finding out Toni was a lesbian, and flew in from San Juan to persuade her to leave Clarice and bring Raffi home with them. Of course they went back empty-handed, though lately Toni seems to be making progress with them.

One of the most frequent questions I get asked is why was Clarice and Toni's baby a boy? I think a lot of readers just expected they'd have a girl and the strip would go on being a women-only space. Partly I made him a boy because statistically, most babies conceived through A.I. are male. But the main reason I made him a boy is that it affords more interesting narrative possibilities. Raffi seems like a pretty sweet, laid-back kid so far, but I haven't really focused on him enough yet to discover his real personality.

For a long time, Ginger was just one of Lois' housemates. It wasn't till almost a year after I introduced her that I gave her an occupation: graduate student in English. She lives in a collective household with Lois and Sparrow. I think of the three of them as mind, body, and spirit respectively, and often play them against one another. After taking ten years to finish her dissertation, it looks like it's going to take Ginger another ten years to find a teaching position. In the meantime, she's eking out a subsistence as an adjunct faculty member at the university. She has some unexplored intimacy issues and tends to freak out when people get too close.

Sparrow started out as arguably the most cartoony of my characters—a flaky, crystal-wearing therapy junkie. Somewhere along the line, though, she settled down enough to become the director of a battered women's shelter. For a long time Sparrow didn't seem to have any romantic attachments, but then in 1993 she got involved with June. I never seemed to find the time to explore their relationship, and June was starting to feel like dead weight, so I broke them up in 1997. Sparrow came to life a little bit more after that, updated her hairdo, and started chafing at the lack of privacy her communal living situation offered. As I write this, she's thinking about giving men another try.

Sparrow

Jezanna runs Madwimmin Books, where Mo, Lois, and Thea work. I guess it's kind of odd that an African-American woman would have only white women working for her, but I didn't think of that when I first introduced her. I hate that stereotype of the big, wise black woman who nurtures all the spiritually deprived white people around her, so I've made Jezanna the polar opposite of maternal. She's a tough boss, runs the bookstore in a strictly hierarchical manner—no "collective" business for her—and is pretty out of touch with her feelings. We never saw much of her personal life until quite recently. She's in a long-distance relationship with Audrey, her mother's oncology nurse, who she met while her mother recuperated from a mastectomy.

Jezanna

Harriet

Thea

Sydney

Since Harriet split with Mo in 1992, I've attempted to show how they've slowly rebuilt a friendship. She's more of a background character now, but I try not to lose touch with her altogether because I have a real fondness for her. And despite the fact that she's been broken up with Mo for longer than they were together in the first place, a lot of readers seem to share that fondness. Harriet's a real *mensch*, very unflappable and dependable. She's worked for the state Department of Human Rights forever. For a couple of years she was involved with Ellen, a charismatic, high-powered community leader who was the exact opposite of Mo (except I intentionally drew them to look a little bit alike).

Thea began working at the bookstore in 1991. I mentioned that she was an artist when I first introduced her. But that detail has gone unexplored, thanks to the merciless editing I'm forced to employ in order to fit my story into nine or ten tiny panels every other week. I didn't specify exactly what her disability was for quite a while—we just knew that she had good days when she could get around on crutches and bad days when she used a chair. I did this partly because I wanted to present her disability as just a part of who she was, and also because I could never think of a way to mention it that wasn't heavy-handed. Finally, it surfaced in the context of the story after Sydney moved to town: Thea revealed that the two of them had been lovers ten years before, and that when she was diagnosed with multiple sclerosis, Sydney freaked out and dumped her.

Sydney, the evil women's studies professor, is a relatively recent addition to the cast. I was getting bored writing about such paragons of virtue all the time, and wanted a character who was really insufferable. Sydney's over-it-all postmodern attitude has added a fresh and much needed perspective to the strip: she goes to the annual women's craft fair not out of community loyalty but because she's trying to find a joke gift for an ex. I also designed Sydney as an antagonistic love interest for Mo, who was shocked when she found out how badly Sydney had treated Thea in the past. But somehow Sydney persuaded Mo that she'd redeemed herself. I'm not so easily convinced, however.

Carlos is the second male character to appear in the strip, after Raffi. There are lots of reasons why, for a long time, I didn't have men in the strip except as background characters. But the main one is that it seemed like there were already enough male characters in the world. I wanted men to read my strip and be forced to identify with the women characters, the way women and people of color are expected to identify with the zillions of "universal" white male protagonists in comics, books, tv, movies, and everywhere else. But I didn't want Raffi to be all alone, so I brought Carlos on the scene. He's a friend of Toni's from a queer Latino group they were in together. I haven't been able to give a lot of time to his character yet. All we really know is that he's out of work, he lives with his lover, Daniel, and he loves Raffi.

Carlos

Introducing Raffi to the strip injected it with some much-needed generational diversity. But the predominance of thirty-something characters was still a problem. I brought Anjali in as an intern at the bookstore to help liven things up. She's a high school student, has her own zine, carries Emma Goldman in her Hello Kitty backpack, and created the bookstore's web site. She'll probably go off to college soon, though, so I'll lose her valuable perspective. I guess I could keep bringing in new interns. Maybe they'll be like Murphy Brown's secretaries—a colorful, constantly changing stream of sixteen-year-olds.

Anjali

THROWING SHADE

I've never used any kind of shading to differentiate the skin color of my African-American characters. When I was starting to draw "Dykes," I noticed that a lot of white cartoonists, on the rare occasions when they included people of color at all, used shading as the only way of indicating that a character was black. They would basically draw a white person, give them curly black hair, and fill in their faces with grey shading. So I tried to convey my characters' race by focusing on their features.

Many of the shading styles I've seen other cartoonists use tend to obscure the characters' faces or seem prohibitively labor-intensive.

Howard Cruse, in his graphic novel *Stuck Rubber Baby*, creates an incredibly rich palette of skin tones, shading even his white characters with a delicate cross-hatching. But assuming I could find the extra time (and skill and patience), that level of fine detail isn't really consistent with my drawing style.

Condensed Dykes To Watch Out For

I took a quaalude once in college, and under its influence carried out a project for my drawing class. The assignment was to present "different views of yourself so as to confront the problems of time and space." It was a very conceptual class, and it never occurred to me to pick up a pencil and actually draw a self-portrait. Instead, I decided to show myself as a product of western civilization by xeroxing a timeline of history that I found in a book in the library, then taping it all together in a fifteen-foot-long scroll. As I stood there feeding nickels into the copier, I was astonished by my brilliance. But I was also fascinated by the timeline itself and the way it absorbed the chaos of history, compressed it into pivotal events, then displayed it graphically. Scanning the chart, I could grasp the unfolding of time with an immediacy that a textual history couldn't have conveyed.

When I returned to the dorm with my sheaf of copies my roommate informed me that you were supposed to have sex when you took quaaludes. But if I had had sex, I might never have gotten the idea for the next section of this book.

On the following pages runs a timeline charting noteworthy events in my characters' lives over the course, to date, of the comic strip. No drugs were involved this time, but it was still fun to boil down eleven years of comic strips into eleven pages.

There's a line in the chart for real-life events that made their way into the comic strip, like presidential elections, marches on Washington, and the Iran/Contra hearings. I've included drawings of stray artifacts that showed up in various episodes, such as Lois's leather jacket and Sparrow's crystal necklace, to help show the ebb and flow of trends in fashion. Literary trends can be followed in the Madwimmin Books line of the chart, which contains various titles that have appeared on the shelves there over the years.

But the bulk of the timeline graphs milestones in the characters' lives: relationships, flings, jobs, etc. This is a very useful resource in case you're wondering about the precise succession of Lois's *divertissements*, or if the question of when, exactly, Mo entered therapy ever comes up in conversation. The timeline also serves as an extremely abridged version of the entire "Dykes To Watch Out For" saga to date, so if you're in a rush, you can get the gist of the story without wasting valuable time reading all my books.

Iran/Contra

Nat'l March on Washington for Lesbian & Gay Rights

1987

Gets a regrettable haircut and loses her proofreading job.

Falls for Harriet.

Six months later, finally beds Harriet.

Mo

In her first year of law school, Clarice pulls Mo's leg about becoming a corporate tax lawyer.

Our heroic couple is so busy they miss their fifth anniversary.

Clarice & Toni

Naomi is Lois's latest conquest.

Sparrow, Ginger, & Lois

U.S. OUT OF El Salvador

Mo starts work as a cashier. $5 an hour, no benefits.

Mad-wimmin Books

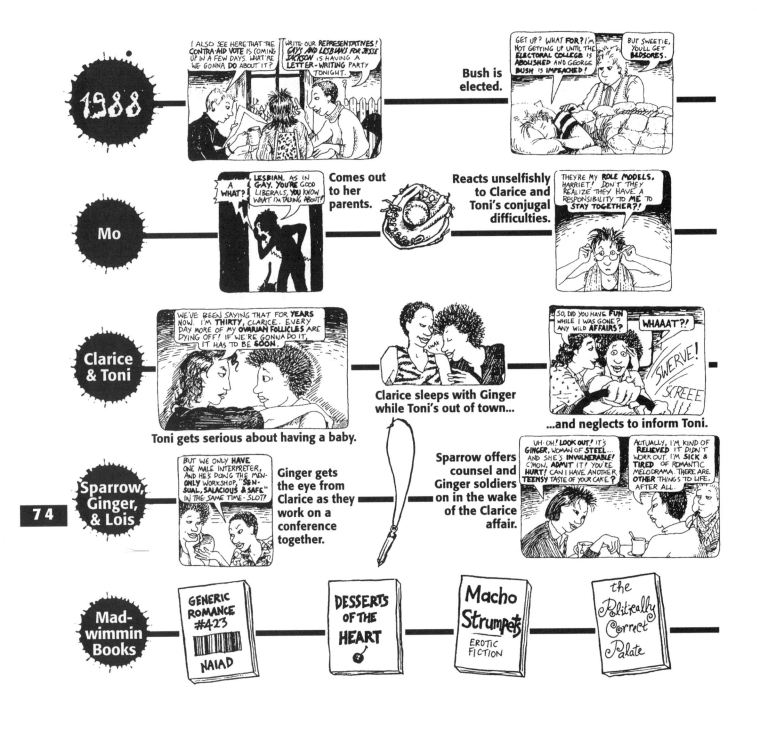

1990

Mo

Things with Harriet start going from bad...

...to worse.

So they decide to move in together.

Clarice & Toni

Clarice plights her troth...

...and the vows are sworn in the back yard.

Sparrow, Ginger, & Lois

Ginger is deeply concerned about the military build-up in the Persian Gulf.

Lois joins Queer Nation.

Mad-wimmin Books

Mo can't accept that the times they are a-changin'.

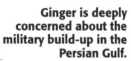

The Gulf War is televised.

WE'LL BE BACK WITH MORE EXCITING DESCRIPTIONS OF MISSILES, PAYLOADS, AND EXPLOSIONS AFTER THIS WORD FROM OUR SPONSOR, GENERAL ELECTRIC.

THE WAR CHANNEL!

Clarence Thomas is confirmed to the Supreme Court.

Genetic research yields startling new information.

The Distress
STRANGE CLUSTER OF BRAIN CELLS FOUND IN STRAIGHT MEN

1991

DRAFT NEIL BUSH WHEN HE GETS OUTTA JAIL!

REFUSE TO PAY TAXES? DO THEY LET YOU DO THAT?!

Mo on the ramparts.

JUSTIFY MY LOVE

Mo hitting a plateau in therapy.

Mo

UNIVERSAL COMMERCIAL CODE

Clarice graduates from law school, passes the bar, and begins clerking for a judge.

OKAY. ZNNNK!

CLAR-EECE!

Toni starts charting her ovulation cycle.

Clarice & Toni

Lois inadvertently schtups one of Ginger's students.

YOU DIDN'T TELL ME YOU LIVE WITH MS. JORDAN! SHE'S WAY COOL! ALL THE DYKES IN MY LIT CLASS ARE LIKE TOTALLY CRUSHED OUT ON HER!

MS. JORDAN?

Ginger meets Malika at the National Lesbian Conference and embarks on a long-distance relationship.

Sparrow, Ginger, & Lois

DON WHINE IN THE VILLAGE

Sexing the Fruit Cocktail

YOU WHAT?

WHO?!

YEAH. I KNOW IT'S HARD TO BELIEVE, MO, BUT THE WHEELCHAIR DOESN'T IMPAIR MY HEARING AT ALL.

Mad-wimmin Books

Mo and Lois vie for a new position at the store...

...but Jezanna hires someone else.

After a brief adjustment period, Thea is accepted by the natives.

1992

L.A. riots

Clinton is elected.

Mo

Mo finally pushes Harriet over the edge.

And after one last tango...

...Harriet is spotted with a new consort.

Clarice & Toni

The insemination begins.

Five months and a considerable sum later, the results are in.

Sparrow, Ginger, & Lois

Malika arrives for a long-awaited visit.

Lois reluctantly turns thirty...

...and changes her hairstyle.

Mad-wimmin Books

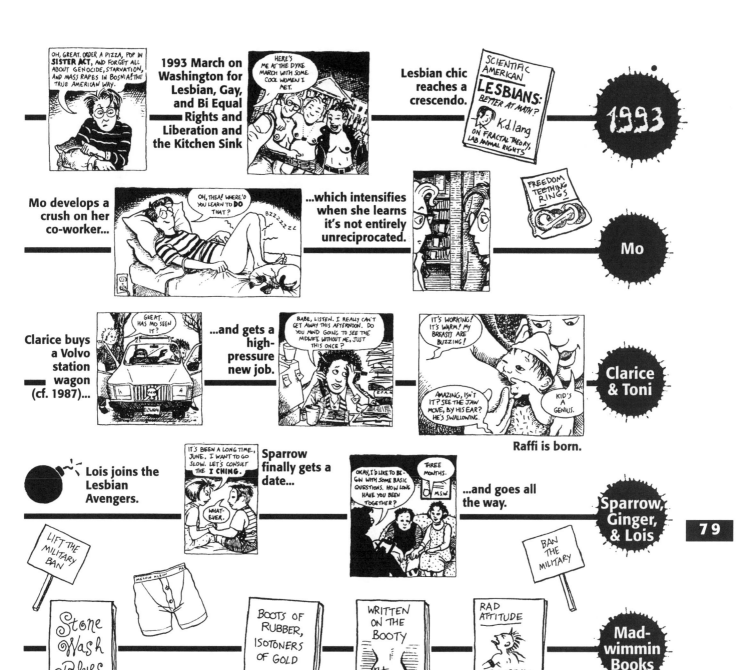

1994

The gals travel to NYC for Stonewall 25.

Mo

Our heroine begins to feel her age...

HAVE YOU NOTICED, SUDDENLY THERE'S ALL THESE **YOUNG DYKES** EVERYWHERE? WHERE'D THEY **COME** FROM?!

THE MALL?

...and has a fling with a precocious young writer.

FORGET ABOUT THE BOOK REVIEW.

OFFICE

Mo and Thea's crush dissipates after a flat New Year's Eve kiss.

Clarice & Toni

HE CAN'T GO TO BED! IT'S ONLY SEVEN! I LEFT A TON OF WORK UNFINISHED JUST SO I'D GET TO SPEND SOME TIME WITH HIM!

WHINE.

Clarice is working 60-hour weeks.

Toni starts hanging out with Gloria.

YEAH, I'LL HAVE TO CALL LOIS LATER FOR THE DETAILS. JEEZ, I CAN'T REMEMBER THE LAST TIME I HAD SEX IN A SEMI-PUBLIC PLACE.

TELL ME ABOUT IT. I KNEW HAVING A KID WOULD CHANGE THINGS, BUT I NEVER EXPECTED ANA AND I WOULD BECOME A LESBIAN BED DEATH STATISTIC.

80

Sparrow, Ginger, & Lois

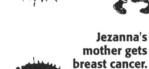

ZIP!

Lois befriends Sonya.

MEANWHILE, IN SECAUCUS...

EXCUSE ME...YOU MADE SOME VERY INTERESTING POINTS IN THAT LAST WORKSHOP. YOU'RE QUITE A SPEAKER!

7th ANNUAL CONFERENCE FROM SILENCE TO CELEBRATION Beyond the 28 Days

WHY, THANK YOU! YOU WEREN'T HALF BAD YOUR-SELF! UH... I'M GINGER.

Schedule

Ginger has another conference fling...

L-**LIVE** TOGETHER? JEEZ, BABE...YOU KNOW HOW IMPORTANT MY WORK IS TO ME RIGHT NOW. I'M TOTALLY WRAPPED UP IN MY DISSERTATION! COULDN'T WE TALK ABOUT THIS LATER?

WE DON'T HAVE TO. THAT'S ALL I NEEDED TO HEAR.

...and can't seem to commit to Malika.

Mad-wimmin Books

Jezanna's mother gets breast cancer.

THERE'S NOTHING LEFT TO SAY! I TOLD HER A THOUSAND TIMES, "**MAMA!** YOU NEED TO GET A **MAMMO-GRAM!**" I EVEN MADE APPOINTMENTS! DID SHE KEEP THEM? NO, SHE DID NOT!

The BOOK of SHORT LESBIAN PENGUIN STORIES

The new Bunns and Noodle superstore starts drawing customers away.

THEY SERVE GREAT CAPPUCCINO, TOO. ER... SO I'VE HEARD.

CLARICE! THAT PLACE IS OWNED BY A GIGANTIC CORPORATION! BOOKS ARE JUST A COMMODITY TO THEM, LIKE SMALL APPLIANCES, OR... OR **HEALTH INSURANCE!** THEY DON'T CARE ABOUT LITERATURE, OR IDEAS, OR COMMUNITY! HOW CAN YOU SHOP THERE?!

MO, YOU'RE SCARING THE KID.

Clarice plots legal strategies.

O.J. The trial...

...and the verdict.

Mo takes to drink after a rupture with Deirdre...

...and gets momentarily besotted with a bad poet.

A rapprochement is forged with Harriet.

Mo

Clarice grows increasingly distracted by her work.

Toni grows increasingly distracted by Gloria.

But eventually they both come to their senses.

Clarice & Toni

Ginger's having trouble concentrating on her dissertation.

Lois and Sparrow have an adventure in babysitting.

Sparrow, Ginger, & Lois

81

Heather Has One Sperm Donor

Jezanna takes up with her mother's oncology nurse.

Mad-wimmin Books

1996

Mo's worried about assimilation.

Mo

Girl meets girl.

Girl antagonizes girl.

Girl wears girl down.

Clarice & Toni

Our doughty moms hire a lawyer and pursue second-parent adoption of Raffi.

Their home-study caseworker shows up on the same day as Toni's homophobic parents.

82

Sparrow, Ginger, & Lois

Lois starts taking Prozac...

...which seems to be having an inhibitive effect on her relations with Babette.

Ginger's procrastination reaches fever pitch.

ANI RULES

Mad-wimmin Books

Lois has an idea to help boost sales.

My Lover Used to be a Woman

A youthful intern joins the staff.

Ellen comes out...

...but business seems to go on pretty much as usual.

Raffi flaunts the Disney boycott by demanding to see - Hercules.'

1997

Mo gets some new underwear...

...in the nick of time.

But the course of true love never did run smooth.

Mo

Raffi has two state-approved mommies.

Clarice is persuaded to go househunting.

Raffi starts preschool and Toni gets a job.

Clarice & Toni

Ginger finally finishes her dissertation.

Lois switches antidepressants.

Sparrow gets a new haircut...and our housemates may lose house and home.

Sparrow, Ginger, & Lois

83

Madwimmin is saved by a benefit of questionable nature.

Jezanna's mother dies.

Madwimmin Books

The Factory Tour

Sometimes I feel like I'm a slave to my characters. They run the show, and I just function as their scribe, inking out the vicissitudes of their lives while chained to my drawing board. I explored this sensation to its logical end in the following 1995 fantasia about how "Dykes To Watch Out For" cartoons get produced. This "factory tour" was created for a computer slide show screensaver that I sold through my cartoon merchandise mail-order business.

The "Mo" boxer shorts, diapers, and tea towels on display in the factory store at the end of this piece poke fun at the various shamelessly commercial items I've peddled over the years.

I started selling postcards of my work in 1985 with a hand-drawn flier that I sent to a few dozen people. Over the years I added T-shirts, posters, coffee mugs, buttons, and other items to my line of schlock, and the catalog grew to twelve typeset pages with a glossy two-color cover. I had some reluctance about hawking such essentially useless junk to people, as well as some scruples about exploiting the integrity of my work by plastering it on mouse pads. But I liked playing store, and it was a nice way to interact with my readers.

My keen business acumen eventually led me, however, to realize that the whole venture was barely breaking even, plus I was wasting a lot of time producing catalogs and talking to T-shirt companies that would have been better spent drawing. So I closed up shop in 1997.

95

Chapter four
Calendar Girls

On the following pages are comics culled from the calendars I created from 1990 to 1997. For the first two years, all my calendar cartoons were about Mo, Clarice, Toni, and the other "DTWOF" characters. It was much more difficult for me to write the calendar than it was to write my regular, ongoing episodes. The calendar comics had to be self-contained. There was no spilling over into the next installment—each page was going to hang on people's walls for a month at a time. That meant I couldn't write any of the long, protracted dramas I'd gotten so fond of in my strip. I also couldn't write about current events: they'd be dated before the calendar even hit the bookstores. Since current events and the characters' intrigues were my two main sources of subject matter, the calendar cramped my style pretty severely.

Then, with the 1992 calendar, I began adding comics that weren't about Mo or any of my other regular characters. Many of these pieces were inspired by the *Mad Magazine* cartoons I had grown up with. There are quizzes, "do" and "don't" lists, field guides, parodies, limericks, and games. These kinds of cartoons seemed to lend themselves much more easily to the one-shot format of the calendar page than the Mo-centric

Cleo Baldshein practicing guerilla therapy in "Silly Putty Syndrome," *More Dykes To Watch Out For.* **Cleo is one of my anagrammatic alter egos. Her compatriots Heloise C. Bland and Delilah B. Scone contributed to my first book.**

strips did. And it was a relief to get a break from Mo's high-mindedness, to be able to play around with some of the frothier ideas I'd been stockpiling on napkins and chopstick wrappers over the years. These "non-Mo" calendar strips were also a throwback to the early years of "Dykes To Watch Out For," before I came up with my regular cast.

Included among the "non-Mo" strips are five "Cleo Baldshein, Guerilla Therapist" cartoons. Cleo actually made her first appearance not in the calendar, but in a regular "Dykes To Watch Out For" strip in 1986 called "Silly Putty Syndrome." This turned out to be the last episode before I started working with recurring characters and an ongoing story line. Mo and Lois debuted the next month.

I've always had a soft spot for Cleo because of that watershed strip. Not only did she herald the transformation of "Dykes" from a monthly cartoon meditation on different aspects of lesbian culture into a bi-weekly, character-driven narrative, she also deflowered me.

Up until "Silly Putty Syndrome," I don't recall ever suffering over my comic strip. I might have sweated the drawing a bit, but I never doubted that I was capable of creating these cartoons, and I had no absolutely no awareness of any yawning void threatening to swallow me whole. This deadline, however, was different. A few days before the strip was due, I brought my sketchbook along on a weekend getaway with my lover, figuring I'd find some time between having sex and taking saunas to crank out the latest installment.

I found myself, instead, sitting in our rented cabin, staring at a blank sheet of paper with mingled sensations of nausea and impending doom. I was too panicked to have sex. The sauna gave me heart palpitations. And besides, I didn't have time for nonessentials. There were newspapers expecting this comic strip. Possibly even readers waiting for it. But there was no comic strip. How had I gotten myself into this?

At some point during those hellish two days—I'm not sure exactly how—I managed to wring Cleo Baldshein from the dry sponge of my brain. But it was the beginning of the end with that particular girlfriend, and my creative process has never been the same.

I understood later that I'd had an anxiety attack. While I've learned to manage the stress, I've never been able to regain that "beginner's mind," that state of blissful ignorance before I realized exactly how hard it was to do what I was doing. I lost my creative innocence to Cleo Baldshein, M.S.W.

Ironically, I created Cleo before I'd actually done any therapy. After beginning my own laborious and gradual psychotherapeutic odyssey, I began to yearn for Cleo's bracing, quick-fix approach, and resurrected her for five more "workshops" in the calendar comics (see pages 123, 149, 153, 163, and 182).

I found it extremely draining to come up with twelve new cartoons per year in addition to my regular strip and other projects. It became an annual ritual to essentially lose the month of March as I tried to finish the calendar (for distribution purposes, it had to be printed by June) in a crazed binge of all-night workfests. The effort started to seem disproportionate to the limited income fetched by a product with such a short shelf-life, and the 1997 calendar was my last.

The calendar pages are arranged chronologically, which is a good way to see just how bad my drawing used to be. Some of these early comics are pretty embarassing, and I left out a few of the more extreme duds. Trust me, you're not missing anything. Four of the calendar cartoons appeared earlier (see pages 34, 55, 56, and 57) so they're not included here. With these few exceptions, the annual calendar strips follow.

I CAN'T **HELP** IT! HOW CAN YOU **NOT**?

Early bad drawing. Neanderthal Mo, circa 1989

NO LACK OF RESOLVE

Panel 1:
WHAT HAVE YOU BEEN DOING ON MY COMPUTER ALL EVENING?

INPUTTING MY **NEW YEAR'S RESOLUTIONS**. HAVE YOU FINISHED YOURS YET?

TIK TIKKA TIK

Panel 2:
ME?! OH, OF COURSE! THEY'RE AT THE STONECUTTER'S RIGHT NOW, BEING **ETCHED** IN **MARBLE**!

Panel 3:
JOKE IF YOU LIKE, HARRIET. THIS HAPPENS TO BE A VERY IMPORTANT TRADITION TO ME.

Panel 4:
SO I SEE. "NUMBER 22. LEARN MORE ABOUT POLITICS IN THE MIDDLE EAST. 23. BECOME FLUENT IN SPANISH. 24. FLOSS REGULARLY. 25. COME OUT TO AUNT LOUISE..."

— RIP

Panel 5:
WELL THAT'S GREAT, MO. BUT I GUESS I'M JUST NOT A GOAL-ORIENTED KINDA GAL. I **LIKE** BEING IRRESOLUTE!

AW, DON'T WORRY, SWEETIE! I'LL HELP YOU MAKE YOUR LIST!

Panel 6:
YOUR FIRST RESOLUTION COULD BE TO ASK FOR A **RAISE** AT **WORK**. YOU **KNOW** THEY DON'T PAY YOU WHAT YOU'RE WORTH!

TIKKA TIKKA TIK

Panel 7:
...AND NUMBER TWO COULD BE TO BECOME MORE **POLITICALLY ACTIVE**!

OKAY! AND MAKE NUMBER THREE TO FIND A NEW GIRLFRIEND WHO ISN'T CONTROLLING, ANAL-RETENTIVE, OR DRIVEN BY **LIBERAL GUILT**.

Panel 8:
THERE YOU GO! SEE, IT'S **EASY** ONCE YOU GET STARTED! DOES 'ANAL-RETENTIVE' HAVE A HYPHEN?

100

A groovy T-shirt company approached me about printing *Does anal-retentive have a hyphen?* on one of their shirts. It ended up getting advertised in one of those catalogs geared to public radio listeners, and we sold quite a few.

HEART THROB
CLARICE, REMEMBER THE FIRST BATH WE TOOK TOGETHER?
VIVIDLY! WHEN WE WERE FINISHED, THERE WAS MORE WATER LEAKING THROUGH YOUR DOWNSTAIRS NEIGHBOR'S CEILING THAN IN THAT DINKY TUB!
-SIGH- WE WERE SO IN LOVE THEN.
SO WHAT'S THIS?! AN EIGHT-YEAR MEANINGLESS FLING? WE'RE STILL IN LOVE!
OF COURSE WE ARE. BUT... IT'S NOT THE SAME. DON'T YOU MISS HOW PASSIONATE AND INTENSE IT USED TO BE?
WELL, YEAH... I GUESS... BUT MAKING LOVE IS SO MUCH MORE MEANINGFUL AND INTIMATE NOW.
YEAH, RIGHT. MEANINGFUL, INTIMATE, AND BORING. SAME TIME, SAME PLACE, SAME TECHNIQUE! IT'S SO PREDICTABLE.
PREDICTABLE, HUH? CARE TO PREDICT WHAT I GOT FOR YOUR VALENTINE'S PRESENT?
A PRESENT? FOR ME? WHAT?!
I'LL GIVE YOU A HINT. IF WE WERE USING IT RIGHT NOW, WE'D PROBABLY ELECTROCUTE OURSELVES.
FROM THE GLEAM IN YOUR EYE, I GET THE FEELING IT'S NOT A SALAD SHOOTER.

Great Expectations

YOU SURE ARE DRAGGIN' YOUR TAIL TODAY, GIRL!

YEAH, MY PARENTS CALLED ME UP LAST NIGHT TO PESTER ME ABOUT WHAT THEY CALL MY "CAREER PLANS".

JUST TELL 'EM, "BUT MOM, DAD! I'M A PROFESSIONAL LESBIAN! IT SURE SHUTS MY PARENTS UP FAST!

WHAT'S WRONG WITH WORKING IN A WOMEN'S BOOKSTORE? SEEMS LIKE A PERFECTLY RESPECTABLE CAREER TO ME.

AW, YOU KNOW, JEZANNA! THEY EXPECT ME TO GO TO GRADUATE SCHOOL AND GET A JOB MAKING $40,000 THAT I HAVE TO WEAR A SUIT TO, AND THEN WIN THE NOBEL PRIZE!

WELL, I DUNNO ABOUT $40,000 BUT IF IT WOULD MAKE YOU HAPPY, YOU CAN WEAR A SUIT TO WORK HERE.

VERY FUNNY. I DON'T KNOW WHY I LET THEM MAKE ME FEEL SO BAD... I LOVE MY JOB!

Y'KNOW, MY FOLKS STILL EXPECT ME TO MARRY SOME MAN... AND UNTIL I DO, THEY'RE GONNA TREAT ME LIKE A CHILD. NEVER MIND I RUN A SUCCESSFUL, INDEPENDENT BOOKSTORE!

THERE'S TWO KINDS OF PARENTS: THE ONES WHO WANT YOU TO BE JUST LIKE THEM, AND THE ONES WHO WANT YOU TO DO EVERYTHING THEY NEVER DID. AND THERE'S NO PLEASING EITHER OF THEM.

WHICH KIND DO YOU HAVE?

ACTUALLY, I TRAINED MINE EARLY NOT TO EXPECT ANYTHING AT ALL WHEN I REFUSED TO FLY UP FROM BROWNIES TO GIRL SCOUTS.

AWRIGHT! DOWNWARDLY MOBILE AT AGE 8!

103

Obviously this was written pre-Hothead Paisan, or Mo might not have felt compelled to voice such kneejerk pacifism.

This strip reminds me of how in one Sherlock Holmes tale, Dr. Watson's war wound is in his arm, and in another it's in his leg. I forgot that I gave Clarice a tattoo in this strip, and she's been tattooless all the times I've drawn her naked since.

111

This was written B.E. (Before "Ellen"), but Mo still feels exactly the same way.

Another dated strip. Lately, Lois has become a bit more exhibitionistic about her drag king tendencies.

Culture SHOCK

THE MUSIC FESTIVAL IS OVER AND OUR HEROINES BEGIN THEIR RE-ENTRY INTO THE PATRIARCHY!

PHEW! THAT WAS FUN, BUT FIVE DAYS IS ABOUT AS MUCH **NATURE** AND **WOMON-ENERGY** AS I CAN STAND!

IT'S ALWAYS SO WEIRD COMING BACK TO CIVILIZATION... LIKE, ISN'T IT FUNNY TO SEE A **MAN** DRIVING THAT TRACTOR INSTEAD OF A **SHIRTLESS WOMAN** WITH **DREDLOCKS**?

YEAH...AND ISN'T IT STRANGE TO SEE SEXIST BILLBOARDS FOR CARCINOGENIC CONSUMER ITEMS?

...AND RIGHT-TO-LIFE BUMPERSTICKERS, AND GUN RACKS IN THE BACK OF PICK-UP TRUCKS.

I GUESS NONE OF YOU ARE IN THE MOOD FOR A LITTLE **TOP 40**?

DON'T TOUCH THAT RADIO, LOIS! IT'S IMPORTANT TO ACCLIMATE **SLOWLY!** ONE BAR OF BRUCE SPRINGSTEEN AND WE COULD GET THE **BENDS**!

OKAY, OKAY. NO RADIO. SAY, I'M GETTING **HUNGRY.** ANYONE FOR **MCDONALD'S**?

LOIS, DON'T YOU **DARE**! HERE. I MADE PLENTY OF **TAHINI** AND **SPROUT SANDWICHES** AT BREAKFAST THIS MORNING.

GAG ME! SPARROW, DO YOU SERIOUSLY EXPECT ME TO EAT A SANDWICH WITH **GIANT GREEN SPERMS** HANGING OUT OF IT?

A **QUARTER-POUNDER** WITH **CHEESE**, ON THE OTHER HAND, EXUDES A PARTICULARLY NURTURING, **FEMININE** KIND OF ENERGY, DON'T YOU THINK?

116

THE STAR

MO IS PRACTICALLY **BESIDE** HERSELF IN ANTICIPATION OF A READING AT MADWIMMIN BOOKS BY HER FAVORITE LESBIAN **NOVELIST, BIANCA BROMIDE!**

PHEW! MO, COULD YOU SET UP THESE REFRESHMENTS QUICK? BIANCA'LL BE HERE ANY SECOND.

I CAN'T **WAIT** TO MEET HER!

DIET **ROTSI?!** WHAT'S THIS FOR? IS THE BATHROOM SINK CLOGGED AGAIN?

NO, IT'S FOR BIANCA. SHE NEEDS IT WHEN SHE READS. UH-OH! HERE SHE IS!

BIANCA BROMIDE DRINKS **DIET ROTSI?!**

...AND THIS IS MY ASSISTANT, MO... A **BIG FAN** OF YOURS!

HOW NICE. JO, COULD YOU PUT MY COAT IN A SAFE PLACE AND GET ME MY DRINK?

UM, HI!

HMM... SHE'S NOT AS **CUTE** AS HER PICTURE..

HERE YOU GO. Y'KNOW, I MUST'VE READ **LOVE'S LAVENDER LIMBO** SIX TIMES! I REALLY IDENTIFY WITH YOUR CENTRAL METAPHOR OF MARIANNE'S **CODEPENDENCE** AS THE INTESTINAL **PARASITE** SHE PICKS UP IN THE YUCATAN!

YES, THAT WAS VERY CLEVER. SO TELL ME, FLO... WHERE DO YOU GO FOR WINE, **WOMEN** AND **SONG** IN THIS BURG? I'M IN THE MOOD FOR A LITTLE **ACTION** IF YOU KNOW WHAT I MEAN.

ACTION? WHADDAYA MEAN?! WHAT ABOUT YOUR COMMITTED RELATIONSHIP WITH YOUR **DEVOTED PARTNER** OF 12 YEARS!

HEY, WHAT SHE DOESN'T KNOW WON'T HURT HER! HOW ABOUT A **REFILL?**

SO, WHAT'S IT LIKE TO MEET YOUR IDOL? DID SHE SIGN YOUR BOOK?

CAN I TRADE THIS IN FOR A PAIR OF EARRINGS?

Dyke O' the Month

Admit it. There's a part of you that's oddly jealous of all those beefcake and cheesecake calendars that gay men and straight people get to choose from each year. You may thank the goddess **OUR** sexuality hasn't been **CHEAPENED** and **COMMODIFIED** like theirs, but underneath that highly-evolved feminist exterior, you'd give your "erotic in nature" video for a really sexy lesbian calendar.

Oh, there've been attempts -- wholesome, clean-shaven gals on California beaches and women with scary haircuts doing peculiar things in leather --- but where's the down-home, earthy, womanly sensuality that makes being a lesbian so dang much fun? That's what we've tried to capture in this portfolio of erotic lesbian calendars for 1992 — and we hope you won't be disappointed!

Butch Babes fixing things around the house

MS. FEBRUARY PROVIDES PLENTY OF FANTASY FODDER AS SHE FIDDLES WITH THE FUSE BOX!

Femmes into Flannel

HERE ARE SOME CUDDLY GALS YOU'LL WANT TO CRAWL RIGHT INTO BED WITH -- FOR A **NAP!**

Camp Counselors of your dreams

RELIVE THE UNBEARABLY TURBID EROTICISM OF YOUR PUBESCENT YEARS WITH THESE TWELVE ALLURING ROLE MODELS!

the **Bearded Lesbian Calendar**

A DOZEN FUZZY, FEARLESS, PHENOMENAL AMAZONS!

BONUS! MS. OCTOBER SHARES HER CREATIVE SOLUTIONS TO PUBLIC RESTROOM CONFRONTATIONS!

LUPPIE LUST

12 TAILORED TYPES TO TITILLATE YOUR TASTEBUDS!

ARE THOSE SHOULDERS **PADDED**... OR DID SHE GET THEM AT THE HEALTH CLUB?

Sultry Social Workers

WATCH THESE IDEALISTIC, UNDERPAID WONDERS AS THEY COPE WITH CRISES! BATTLE BUREAUCRACY! AND SUFFER FROM STRESS!

YOU'VE NEVER **SEEN** SUCH INTEGRITY!

Needless to say, I wrote this cartoon before the lesbian erotica boom.

Great Moments in Lesbian Romance

APRIL 8, 1991. MEREDITH SCHAPIRO TRANSCRIBES THE COMPLETE LYRICS OF ALL THREE FERRON ALBUMS ONTO LORENE HENDRICKS' BACK WITH HER TONGUE IN SIXTEEN HOURS AND FORTY-EIGHT MINUTES.

WHOA, BABE... YOU FORGOT A REFRAIN THERE!

JANUARY 3, 1992. HESTER McKECHNIE, OF KETCHIKAN, ALASKA, AND MARY LOU AINSCOUGH, OF PAHOKEE, FLORIDA, CELEBRATE THE 18TH ANNIVERSARY OF THEIR SUCCESSFUL LONG-DISTANCE RELATIONSHIP. THEIR SECRET?

WE NEVER TALK ON THE PHONE AND ONLY VISIT ON ALTERNATE LEAP YEARS.

AUGUST 30, 1983. JANICE TAKAZAWA AND HERA GLADYSDAUGHTER MAKE PSYCHOTHERAPEUTIC HISTORY WHEN THEY ENTER COUNSELING TOGETHER **BEFORE** THEIR FIRST DATE!

LET'S EXPLORE THE FEELINGS THAT CAME UP FOR YOU WHEN HERA ASKED YOU OUT TO A MOVIE, JANICE.

BAW! WHEN I WAS SIX—SOB!—MY PARENTS LOST ME AT A MATINEE OF "MARY POPPINS!" SNORT!

NOVEMBER 14, 1988. EX-LOVERS ALEXANDRA GOODSPEED AND LOURDES ESPINOZA RESPOND TO ONE ANOTHER'S PERSONAL ADS AND FALL IN LOVE ALL OVER AGAIN.

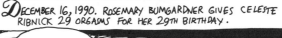

I HAD NO IDEA YOU LIKED TO WALK ALONG THE BEACH!

AND YOU NEVER TOLD ME YOU LIKED CANDLELIT DINNERS AND STIMULATING CONVERSATION!

MAY 29, 1979. WHILE EXPERIMENTING WITH AN ARCANE SEXUAL POSITION KNOWN AS THE "TWO-TOED SLOTH SURROUNDING A RECUMBENT PLATYPUS," MILLICENT ZUMWALT AND LILLIAN GIAMBRUNO SHARE AN INSPIRATIONAL VISION OF THE GODDESS.

I SEE A GLARING WHITE LIGHT...THERE! IT'S HER! SHE'S SURROUNDED BY ARCHES OF SHIMMERING GOLD!

WHAT'S ON THAT SILVER TRAY BY HER THRONE? IT LOOKS LIKE... A LARGE FRIES AND A QUARTER-POUNDER WITH CHEESE!

DECEMBER 16, 1990. ROSEMARY BUMGARDNER GIVES CELESTE RIBNICK 29 ORGASMS FOR HER 29TH BIRTHDAY.

UH-OH. WAS THAT SEVENTEEN OR EIGHTEEN?

121

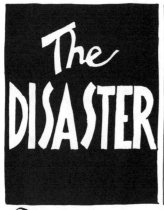

SYNC or SWIM

A Searching and Sibilant Saga of Unsynchronized Sleep Cycles

Scylla is a night person.

Cecily is a morning person.

They met one Sunday afternoon.

SYDNEY SAPERSTEIN, PSYCHIC

Sojourner

At first Scylla found it sweet, how Cecily grew sleepy soon after supper.

I'M SO SMITTEN!

SKNXX.

And for a while, Scylla didn't even mind stirring before sunup!

ISN'T THE SUNRISE SENSUOUS, SWEETIE?

OH, YESSS.

But it soon became a strain. Whenever Scylla felt sexual, she was distressed to find Cecily in a somnolent state.

SANTA FE SAXOPHONE FESTIVAL

SNORE.

And when Cecily sought sex, Scylla would still be slumbering.

SELF LOVE A MANUAL

They solicited a psychotherapist's assistance, and arrived at a satisfactory solution.

SMITH SCHOOL OF SOCIAL WORK

WHY DON'T YOU SIMPLY SCHEDULE SEX FOR WHEN YOU'RE SIMULTANEOUSLY CONSCIOUS?

THAT'LL BE SEVENTY-SIX SMACKERS.

SWELL!

Despite its lack of spontaneity, such a settlement served them splendidly.

HOW WOULD YOU LIKE TO BE SEDUCED AT SEVEN?

SUPER! LET'S DO THE SULTRY SULTANA AND THE SULLEN SUFFRAGETTE! SEE YA!

125

Women of the Festivals
A Partial Field Guide

Did you ever wonder about all those untamed, heathenish-looking amazons at the music festivals? Like, where do they **COME** from? Why don't you ever see them at the **MALL**? And what on **EARTH** do they do for a **LIVING**?! Here's a handy guide to what some of those wild and wooly wimmin are up to during the other 51 weeks of the year.

POSTAL CARRIER

YOUR THERAPIST

ELECTRICIAN

R.N.

CAMPFIRE GIRL

YOUR EX-LOVER'S THERAPIST

TRUCK DRIVER/ ASTROLOGER

COPY SHOP EMPLOYEE/ PERFORMANCE ARTIST

RABBINICAL STUDENT

CITY COUNCIL MEMBER

CAR DEALER

YOUR THERAPIST'S LOVER

ANTHROPOLOGY PROFESSOR

GIMME AN L

A sordid episode from Lois's shady past is about to be made public!

HA!

WHAT? — LOOK AT THIS! I CAN'T BELIEVE IT!

MEMORIES '78

LOIS MACGIVER

OH MY GODDESS! SHE HAS A FARRAH FAWCETT DO AND EVERYTHING!

GIVE ME THAT YEARBOOK!

NO WAY! A CHEERLEADER! DAMN! MAKES ME WONDER WHAT **ELSE** I DON'T KNOW ABOUT YOU, LOIS!

WOW! WERE YOU EVER HOMECOMING QUEEN? DID YOU OSTRACIZE ALL THE NERDY, UNPOPULAR GIRLS? DID YOU DATE A FOOTBALL PLAYER?

ONLY FOR A COUPLE OF MONTHS! GIMME A BREAK! IT WAS JUST A YOUTHFUL INDISCRETION! THE PEER PRESSURE WAS SOMETHING AWFUL!

I DUNNO, LOIS. YOU LOOK PRETTY DAMN SMUG, WIELDING THOSE POM POMS!

IT WAS JUST A PHASE, I SWEAR! I QUIT THE SQUAD MY SENIOR YEAR AND STARTED WEARING ONLY BLACK CLOTHES AND HAD AN AFFAIR WITH MISS HOLMQUIST, MY MATH TEACHER. NOW GIMME THE BOOK!

YESSIR. THIS IS ONE INTERESTING LITTLE PHOTOGRAPH.

GIVE IT, GINGER!

HELP! I'M BEING MOLESTED BY A TESTY CHEERLEADER! SAVE ME BEFORE SHE GETS HER POM POMS!

RRRR

I can't take credit, unfortunately, for Lois' shady past. A friend came up to me one day and said she'd just gotten this vivid image of Lois as a cheerleader in high school. It sounded about right, so I used it.

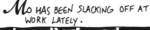

BUT IS THE PEN MIGHTIER THAN THE PAYCHECK?

MO HAS BEEN SLACKING OFF AT WORK LATELY.

MO...YOU'RE DOING IT AGAIN.

HUH? OH! SORRY, JEZANNA! I WAS JUST DUSTING THE SHELVES AND I GOT CARRIED AWAY BY THIS BOOK.

IF YOU DIDN'T OPEN THEM, THEY WOULDN'T CARRY YOU AWAY.

OKAY, OKAY! JEEZ! I JUST NEED A LITTLE MENTAL STIMULATION NOW AND THEN! DUSTING AND SHELVING ALL DAY LONG IS DEATH TO THE CREATIVE IMAGINATION!

CREATIVE IMAGINATION?

YEAH. I'VE DONE SOME WRITING, Y'KNOW. I'D BE PUBLISHED BY NOW IF I'D KEPT IT UP.

OH?

YEAH. Y'KNOW, MAYBE I'LL START AGAIN... JOIN A WRITING GROUP OR SOMETHING.

GREAT. GO FOR IT. AFTER YOU FINISH DUSTING, THOUGH.

JUST WAIT'LL I PUBLISH MY NOVEL, JEZANNA! IT'LL BE A ROMAN À CLEF WHICH BLOWS THE LID OFF THE REPRESSIVE, BEHIND-THE-SCENES WORLD OF FEMINIST BOOKSELLING!

I'M QUAKIN' IN MY BIRKENSTOCKS.

YOU'LL SEE! I'LL TOP THE LESBIAN BESTSELLER LIST FOR MONTHS.

WRITER'S MARKET 1993

YEAH. WELL, EVEN SO, I WOULDN'T QUIT MY DAY JOB. YOU'RE NOT GONNA MAKE YOUR FORTUNE ON ONE BOOK.

I KNOW THAT! I'M NOT TOTALLY NAIVE! IT'S THE MOVIE RIGHTS I'LL CLEAN UP ON.

MO, I'D LET YOU GO IN A MINUTE IF YOU WEREN'T SO AMUSING.

KEEP IT UP, JEZANNA. YOU'RE CRUISING FOR ONE VERY UNFLATTERING PORTRAIT.

LESBO FICTION

A Devoted Companion by Any Other Name...

CONTRARY TO POPULAR BELIEF, ALL LESBIANS ARE **NOT** ASTROLOGY-DEPENDENT, LENTIL-LAPPING LEFTISTS! IN FACT, WE SPAN THE WHOLE GRUESOME GAMUT OF HUMAN POLITICAL POTENTIAL.

SO HOW TO TELL IF YOU'RE **IDEOLOGICALLY COMPATIBLE** WITH THAT SKILLFUL-LOOKING BABE LOUNGING OVER THERE AGAINST THE BAR? NOW IT'S EASY!

QUIZ YOURSELF FIRST, THEN SEE WHO MATCHES UP! IT'S THE...

Convenient *At Home* **POLITICS** *All New!*

TESTING KIT

AVOID THOSE VEXING DIFFERENCES OF OPINION!

HOW ARE YOU EXPRESSING YOUR CONCERN FOR THE ENVIRONMENT?

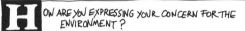

(A) WEARING EXTRA SUNSCREEN AT THE BEACH

(B) BUYING CHECKS WITH THE GREENPEACE LOGO ON THEM

(C) USING "BIODEGRADABLE" PLASTIC TRASH BAGS

(D) RECYCLING GARBAGE INTO SOCIALLY RELEVANT ART OBJECTS

(E) LIVING ON A SOLAR-POWERED, FRAGRANCE-FREE WORM COMPOSTING RANCH

I CALL IT "LAMENT FOR A LANDFILL"

WHICH ANSWER BEST COMPLETES THE FOLLOWING SENTENCE FOR YOU? "PORNOGRAPHY IS _____."

(A) PERVERTED FILTH

(B) A FIRST AMENDMENT RIGHT

(C) KINDA GROSS

(D) SAFE SEX

(E) PERVERTED FILTH

ON OUR BUTTS

LESBIAN ETHICS

FINISH THIS STATEMENT: "MEN ARE _____."

(A) MY ROLE MODELS

(B) OUR BROTHERS

(C) KINDA LOUD

(D) SOMETIMES EDUCABLE

(E) MUTANTS

Café
WOMEN ONLY WEDNESDAYS FROM 8-9

ME OPPRESSIVE? I CRIED WHEN I READ "THE SECOND SEX!"

HOW WOULD YOU BEST DESCRIBE YOUR PERSONAL VISION OF WORLD PEACE?

(A) A STRONG DEFENSE IS THE BEST OFFENSE

(B) EQUAL REPRESENTATION OF WOMEN IN GOVERNMENT

(C) FREE CABLE FOR EVERYONE

(D) ANARCHY

(E) PARTHENOGENESIS

YOUR BIGGEST FEAR IS:

(A) THAT THE MAILMAN WILL SOMEHOW MANAGE TO UNSTAPLE YOUR COPY OF "LESBIAN CONNECTION"

(B) DYKES ON BIKES

(C) NO MORE TOILET PAPER

(D) A BAD HAIRCUT

(E) "LESBIANS" WHO SLEEP WITH MEN

PRIDE MARCH
OUT 3 PROUD

Score Yourself!

A = 5 POINTS, B = 4, C = 3, D = 2, E = 1

YOU'RE A...

21-25   SELF-LOATHING TRAITOR TO YOUR GENDER

16-20   PATHETIC ASSIMILATIONIST PAWN

11-15   COMPLACENT BRAINWASHED DUPE

6-10   RADICAL CHIC POSEUR

1-5   FANATICAL SEPARATIST ZEALOT

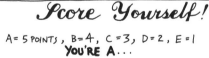

JEANE KIRKPATRICK FAN CLUB

OLIVIA CRUISES

CELTICS

BIG FAG

SEPS DO IT CORRECTLY

This strip inspired "Sentimental Education," the much longer exploration of how all my characters met that appears in *Unnatural Dykes To Watch Out For.*

Mo's Index

Y'KNOW, I JUST DON'T UNDERSTAND HOW **SOME** PEOPLE CAN HANG OUT READING **CARTOONS** WHILE THE WORLD IS GOING TO **HELL** IN A **HANDBASKET** ALL AROUND THEM!

DON'T YOU REALIZE THAT EVERY SECOND YOU STAND THERE, AN ENTIRE **ACRE** OF **RAINFOREST** IS BEING DESTROYED? AND BY THE TIME YOU FINISH READING THIS PAGE, THE AVERAGE SCHOOLCHILD WILL HAVE WATCHED ONE MURDER AND THREE INSTANCES OF SEXIST BEHAVIOR ON TELEVISION?

44% OF MOVIEGOERS ARE IN FAVOR OF COMMERCIALS IN THEATERS, AND FOR EVERY U.S. CITIZEN THERE ARE **17** SQUARE FEET OF **SHOPPING MALL**!

7,000 HARLEQUIN ROMANCE NOVELS ARE SOLD EVERY **HOUR**! "GARFIELD" IS THE MOST WIDELY SYNDICATED CARTOON IN THE WORLD! THE AVERAGE AMERICAN DRINKS **47 GALLONS** OF **SODA** IN A YEAR!

THERE ARE 50% MORE YOUNG REPUBLICANS THAN THERE WERE IN 1980, AND HALF OF LESBIANS WHO'VE BEEN IN RELATIONSHIPS LONGER THAN TEN YEARS HAVE SEX **ONCE A MONTH OR LESS**!

SO?! DON'T JUST **STAND** THERE! **DO** SOMETHING!

KOFF

I WAS JUST ABOUT TO WRITE A LETTER TO MY CONGRESSPERSON.

I WONDER HOW MANY TREES DIED TO MAKE THIS CALENDAR?

HI! THIS IS CINDEE NILSSON WELCOMING YOU TO COVERAGE OF LESBIAN NATION'S HOTTEST NEW SPORTS CRAZE, THE GRUELLING, ACTION-PACKED...

WITH ME IS DEFENDING CHAMPION **OPHELIA GRAFENBERG** TO GIVE US A PREVIEW OF THE RUGGED, FIVE-EVENT COURSE. GLAD TO HAVE YOU WITH US, OPHELIA!

GLAD TO BE HERE, CINDEE!

THE COMPETITION STARTS HERE WITH **THE WHEELCHAIR RACE.** COULD YOU EXPLAIN THAT TO US?

WELL, IT'S A TOUGH FIVE-MILE OB-STACLE COURSE THROUGH A CONGESTED AREA AT RUSH HOUR, CINDEE. THE COMPETITORS WHO USE A CHAIR ALL THE TIME HAVE AN EDGE HERE, OF COURSE, BUT IT'S A REAL CONSCIOUSNESS-RAISER FOR THE REST OF THE PACK!

AS THE RACERS CROSS THE FINISH LINE, THEY DIVE RIGHT INTO THE NEXT EVENT: **COMING OUT TO THE RELATIVE OF THEIR CHOICE.** HERE ARE SOME WOMEN WARMING UP ON COMPLETE STRANGERS!

NEXT COMES WHAT MANY ATHLETES SAY IS THE TRICKIEST PART OF THE COURSE. **FACILITATING A DISCUSSION ON BISEXUALITY!**

THAT'S RIGHT, CINDEE. THE TOPIC CHANGES EACH YEAR, BUT THIS EVENT IS ALWAYS TREACHEROUS! ONE FALSE MOVE AND ALL HELL BREAKS LOOSE. YEP, THE CONTEST HERE DEFINITELY MAKES OR BREAKS YOU.

IF YOUR HAND-EYE COORDINATION IS GOOD, YOU CAN MAKE UP SOME TIME IN THE **RECYCLING SORT.** IT'S TEMPTING TO CUT CORNERS HERE, BUT CONTESTANTS CAN BE DISQUALIFIED IF THEY DON'T REMOVE THE GLOSSY INSERTS FROM THE SUNDAY PAPERS.

FOR THE FINAL EVENT, COMPETITORS DELIVER AN IMPROMPTU CRITIQUE OF **MISOGYNY** IN **POPULAR CULTURE** WHILE SIMUL-TANEOUSLY **REBUILDING** A **CARBURETOR.**

HOW THRILLING! BEST OF LUCK TO YOU TODAY, OPHELIA! AND WE'LL BE RIGHT BACK AFTER THIS WORD FROM OUR SPONSOR!

MEET ME IN THE LOCKER ROOM LATER?

ANYTHING YOU SAY, BABE. I'M POWERLESS AGAINST WOMEN IN SPANDEX.

135

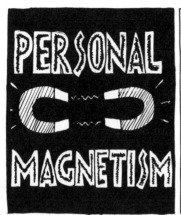

PERSONAL MAGNETISM

Sparrow's revelation astonishes her normally unflappable house-mates.

YOU'VE BEEN DATING A WOMAN YOU MET THROUGH THE **PERSONALS?**

YOU WILD THING, YOU! WHY DIDN'T YOU **TELL** US YOU WERE RUNNING AN AD?!

OH, RIGHT. I'M SURE YOU BOTH WOULD'VE BEEN REALLY SUPPORTIVE. I WANTED TO SEE IF ANYTHING CAME OF IT FIRST.

SO?! **TELL** US ABOUT HER!

OH, SHE'S...SHE'S PERFECT! EVERYTHING I EVER WANTED IN A GIRLFRIEND!

NO KIDDING? YOU ACTUALLY FOUND A CLEAN & SOBER GEMINI ECOFEMINIST WHO WASN'T RAISED CATHOLIC?

NOT ONLY THAT, BUT SHE'S CUTE, HOPELESSLY ROMANTIC, DEVOTED TO SPIRITUAL GROWTH, AND LOOKING FOR A COMMITTED MONOGAMOUS RELATIONSHIP!

SHE'S BEEN HAPPILY SINGLE FOR THE PAST YEAR, SHE'S NOT TORTURED ABOUT ANY OF HER EXES, SHE'S RESOLVING MAJOR ISSUES IN THERAPY, AND HER **SELF-ESTEEM** IS **INTACT!**

WE'RE SO COMPATIBLE! WE'RE BOTH MORNING PEOPLE, WE WORK FOR SOCIAL SERVICE ORGANIZA-TIONS, WE'RE ALLERGIC TO CATS, WE LOVE COUNTRY-WESTERN MUSIC AND HATE TO EXERCISE!

JEEZ, SPARROW! THAT'S INCREDIBLE!

SHE'S DEFINITELY THE GAL FOR YOU!

THERE'S JUST ONE THING.

WE'RE NOT ATTRACTED TO EACH OTHER.

Mo is pretty easy to find, so you can also look for the chess game, the shekere, an axe, Mickey Mouse ears, a bucket, a raccoon, three cowboy hats, seven baseball caps, some alpha waves, and a T-bone steak.

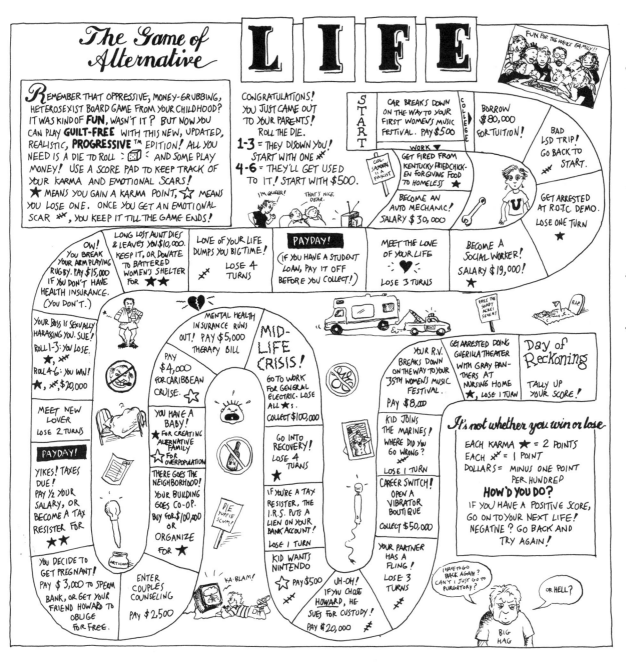

Oral Sex
WE JOIN OUR FAVORITE COUPLE AT AN INTIMATE MOMENT.
A TIP O' THE NIB TO JANET & LISA!
MMM.
UNH.
HOW WAS THAT FOR YOU? BETTER THAN USUAL? OR JUST USUAL?
MNH.
WHAT DID YOU LIKE BEST? WHAT WAS YOUR FAVORITE THING I DID?
MRRM.
I WAS REALLY INTO YOUR CALVES! DID YOU NOTICE HOW I WAS KNEADING THEM? YOU SEEMED TO LIKE IT!
HARRIET, D'YOU FANTASIZE WHEN I'M MAKING LOVE TO YOU? I WAS IMAGINING YOU WERE A RICH COUNTESS SUNBATHING ON YOUR YACHT, AND I WAS YOUR COMELY DECKHAND!
I LIKED HOW YOU ROLLED ME ONTO MY STOMACH AND SUCKED ON MY EAR. WE HAVEN'T DONE THAT POSITION IN A WHILE.
I HAD A REALLY NICE ORGASM. NOT EARTH-SHATTERING, BUT IT WAS NICE. YOU KNOW WHAT I MEAN BY 'NICE?' WHAT WAS YOURS LIKE? OR DID YOU HAVE TWO? I WASN'T SURE. HUH? TELL ME!
SHHH!
HARRIET, I FEEL SO INSECURE WHEN YOU WON'T TALK TO ME AFTER SEX. DID I DO SOMETHING WRONG? DID I RUIN IT?
MO, WILL YOU RELAX? YOU WERE FINE! IT WAS GREAT! I'M JUST FEELING MELLOW... WHEN YOU TALK SO MUCH IT SPOILS THE MOOD!
I KNEW I RUINED IT! DANG! SHOULD I NOT TALK DURING SEX, OR JUST AFTERWARDS? SHOULD I NOT MAKE ANY NOISE AT ALL? IS THAT IT? I'M TOO NOISY? I THOUGHT YOU LIKED THAT... HUH, HARRIET?
MNH!

Sick & Tired of Mo's outfit? Dress her yourself!

VICARIOUSLY INDULGE YOUR WILDEST FASHION FANTASIES IN THIS SAFE, SUPPORTIVE ATMOSPHERE!

WHAT'S WRONG WITH MY REGULAR CLOTHES?

PUT THAT MINI SKIRT ON ME AND YOU DIE!

LET'S UPDATE THAT EYEWEAR

A TRENDY CHAPEAU

FOUNDATION GARMENT

LET'S DO THE LANG THANG! I ♥ K.D.

LET'S SHOCK MOM!

POWER BREAKFAST

THIS IS AN OUTRAGE.

LET'S GO CLUBBING!

CHOOSE A SATIN BUSTIER...

...PASTIES

(FOR PERFORMANCE ART PURPOSES)

USE ELMER'S

...OR A BLACK BRA!

FEELING BRANDOESQUE?

LET'S GET PHYSICAL!

SHADES & TUNES

DON'T FORGET THE ATHLETIC SUPPORTER!

LET'S GET SENSIBLE!

LYCRA

PROTECT THOSE ELBOWS!

FISH-NETS

OR MORE DONNA REED-ISH?

(COLOR THESE PETAL, GRAPEFRUIT, OR LAGOON!)

MIRACLE FABRIC

LET'S CROSS DRESS!

J. SCREW

WHAT'S MO READING? YOU CHOOSE!

A PAIR O' DOCS TO COMPLETE THE LOOK!

INERTIA by CAMILLE PAGLIA

MOBY DICK

Girl Meets Girl NAIAD

MY NEWEST THEORY ABOUT SEX J. LOULAN

UH-OH! HANG ON!

141

IT WAS TWENTY YEARS AGO TODAY

A TIP O'TH' NIB TO NORA & EMILY

*A*H, 1974...

LESBIAN NATION'S **SALAD DAYS!**

CO-OPS, COLLECTIVES, WOMEN'S CENTERS, AND PUBLICATIONS WERE SPRINGING UP LIKE **MUSHROOMS!**

BUT WHAT WERE OUR FAVORITE **TOMATOES** DOING?

WHAT'S GOING ON HERE, ALICE?

WELL, MRS. BRADY, IT SEEMS JAN'S BEEN TRYING TO REMOVE HER FRECKLES SO CLARK WILL ASK HER OUT ON A DATE!

OH, JAN! **FORGET** CLARK! I LOVE YOU JUST THE WAY YOU ARE!

Mo

Lois

I'M TIRED OF PLAYING SONNY & CHER.

OKAY. I HAVE A NEW GAME. IT'S CALLED "GYNECOLOGIST."

Clarice

GIRLS AREN'T STRONG ENOUGH TO **WHAT? HUH?** I CAN'T **HEAR** YOU, DE WAYNE!

UNH! UNCLE!

TONEEE! MY MOM SAID YOU'RE SPOSETA TAKE ME TO DAIRY QUEEN FOR DINNER! I'M HUNGRY NOW! WANNA MILKSHAKE!

TIGER BEAT

Toni

Ginger

ST. JOE'S

RUBYFRUIT

FUNDAMENTALS OF ALGEBRA

Sparrow

WHAT'S YOUR SIGN, BARBIE?

I'M A SCORPIO, SKIPPER! WANNA PLAY WITH MY OUIJA BOARD?

BARBIE

Jezanna

A WOMAN WITHOUT A MAN

IS LIKE A FISH WITHOUT A BICYCLE

142

HOW'S YOUR ETIQUETTE I.Q.?

ANOTHER EDUCATIONAL QUIZ FROM MISS MANNERISM HERSELF,

HELOISE C. BLAND

WHILE MAKING YOUR BED, YOU FIND A PAIR OF YOUR NEW GIRLFRIEND'S UNDERWEAR. WHAT SHOULD YOU DO?
A.) WASH IT AND RETURN IT
B.) RETURN IT UNLAUNDERED, IN A PUBLIC PLACE
C.) NONE OF THE ABOVE

YOU ARE INTRODUCED TO A COUPLE WITH A BABY. WHAT SHOULD YOU DO?
A.) COO INANELY AT IT.
B.) ASK IF THEY WERE AT ALL CONCERNED ABOUT BRINGING A NEW LIFE INTO THIS CORRUPT AND DYING WORLD.
C.) ASK WHICH ONE IS THE MOTHER AND HOW SHE CONCEIVED.

FRESH OR FROZEN?

UPON RUNNING INTO YOUR THERAPIST AT A PUBLIC EVENT, YOU:
A.) RETURN HOME IMMEDIATELY AND TAKE TO YOUR BED
B.) TELL HER THE DREAM YOU HAD LAST NIGHT.
C.) CHAT UP HER LOVER.

SO HOW'D YOU TWO CRAZY KIDS MEET, ANYWAY?

IN CONCERT TONIGHT
Those Fabulous
Flirtations

WHEN MEETING YOUR EX'S NEW LOVER FOR THE FIRST TIME, YOU:
A.) WARMLY EXPRESS THE HOPE THAT YOU'LL ALL BE GOOD FRIENDS.
B.) COMPLETELY IGNORE HER WHILE ASKING YOUR EX-LOVER INTIMATE QUESTIONS ABOUT HER FAMILY.
C.) TAKE HER ASIDE AND ASK HER IF THE EX IS STILL INSATIABLY MULTIORGASMIC.

YOUR DAD'S HEMORRHOIDS... HOW **ARE** THEY?

A STRAIGHT CO-WORKER, UNAWARE THAT YOUR PARTNER OF 15 YEARS IS NOT JUST YOUR ROOMMATE, INVITES YOU OVER TO MEET HER SINGLE BROTHER. YOU:
A.) GENTLY CORRECT HER ASSUMPTION
B.) ASK IF YOU CAN BRING YOUR LOVER
C.) DON'T ASK. JUST DO IT.

NICE TO MEET YOU, DAVID! AND THIS IS NORMA, MY BETTER HALF!

TWO OF YOUR CLOSE FRIENDS ARE GOING THROUGH A MESSY BREAKUP. YOU:
A.) KEEP GOOD BOUNDARIES AND STAY NEUTRAL
B.) GET THEM BOTH TO CONFIDE IN YOU, THEN TELL THEM WHAT THE OTHER ONE SAID.
C.) SEDUCE THE MOST ATTRACTIVE ONE.

FUNNY, THAT'S NOT HOW MARCIA SAID IT HAPPENED!

HOW'D YOU DO?

SCORE 0 POINTS FOR EACH "A," 1 POINT FOR EACH "B," AND 2 POINTS FOR EACH "C."

0-3 GET A LIFE, MS. MILQUETOAST!

4-8 POLITE, BUT PROMISING

9-12 SUCH CHUTZPAH! WITH MANNERS LIKE THIS, YOU'RE SURE TO GO FAR!

143

Because of my calendar deadline, I was writing this strip in February of '93 when Toni had only just gotten pregnant. I had no idea at that point if the baby would be a boy or a girl, or what he/she would look like, so I avoided using names or pronouns and wrapped the kid in a blanket.

I did an earlier version of this strip for an April Fool's edition of *Equal Time,* the lesbian and gay newspaper I worked for in Minneapolis during the late eighties.

Don't be fooled by the Mo red herrings—one's a man, and one's a carnivore (not to mention a femme). I also included Jezanna, Thea, Lois, Ginger, Sparrow, Clarice, Toni, and the baby in this drawing, but they might not be well-drawn enough to be recognizable.

IT WAS YOUR FIRST DATE. YOU NOTICED HER SUBTLE, ELUSIVE SCENT...
THAT EVER-SO-SLIGHT BUT ADORABLE GAP IN HER TEETH...
THE WAY THE NEARLY INVISIBLE DOWN ON HER CHEEK CAUGHT THE LIGHT...
BUT YOU SOMEHOW MANAGED TO OVERLOOK THOSE...

Little Red Flags

MY EX, CASSANDRA, LOVED THIS RESTAURANT. WE ALWAYS CAME HERE FOR OUR ANNIVERSARY. THIS VERY TABLE, IN FACT. SHE WAS SUCH A ROMANTIC. DID I MENTION SHE USED TO BE AN OLYMPIC SWIMMER?

OH, WOW. I CAN'T BELIEVE I FORGOT MY WALLET.

HEY, IT COULD HAPPEN TO ANYONE! YOU CAN PAY ME BACK LATER.

I THINK I'LL HAVE THE LINGUINE WITH CLAM SAUCE.

I DON'T RECOMMEND IT. IT DISAGREED WITH ME ONCE. WHY NOT TRY SOME NICE, PLAIN TOMATO SAUCE? I HOPE THE SERVICE IS QUICK. OUR MOVIE STARTS AT 7:40. I CAN'T **STAND** SITTING THROUGH A FILM IF I'VE MISSED THE PREVIEWS OF COMING ATTRACTIONS! WHERE'S THAT WAITER?

ARE YOU SURE YOU CAN'T STAY A LITTLE LONGER?

I'D LOVE TO, BUT I HAVE TO GET HOME AND FEED MISS PANDORA (DID I SHOW YOU HER PICTURE?) IF I LEAVE HER ALONE FOR TOO LONG, THE LITTLE MINX USES MY BED FOR A LITTER BOX.

IT'S WONDERFUL THAT YOU SPEND SO MUCH TIME WITH YOUR FAMILY. I WISH I WERE THAT CLOSE WITH MINE. HOW DO THEY HANDLE YOU BEING A LESBIAN?

WELL, UH... I'VE BEEN **MEANING** TO TELL THEM... BUT Y'KNOW, IT JUST NEVER SEEMS TO COME UP IN CONVERSATION.

YES, I SOWED SOME WILD OATS IN MY DAY! THREESOMES, MARRIED WOMEN, MY STUDENTS! (HEH HEH) BUT IT'S ALL OUT OF MY SYSTEM NOW. I'M READY TO SETTLE DOWN WITH ONE SPECIAL WOMAN AND CREATE A HOME. YOU KNOW: STABILITY, COMMITMENT, THE WORKS.

Guerilla Mediation

UH-OH! LOCK UP YOUR INNER CHILDREN! IT'S CLEO BALDSHEIN, M.S.W. IN...

WE'VE PROBABLY ALL USED PHRASES LIKE "MAD ABOUT YOU" OR "CRAZY IN LOVE" TO DESCRIBE OUR FEELINGS AT THE BEGINNING OF A RELATIONSHIP.

BUT IF YOU WANNA TALK **DERANGEMENT**, IF YOU WANNA TALK COMING STARK RAVING **UNHINGED**, IT'S THE **END** OF THE RELATIONSHIP THAT BEARS INVESTIGATION.

WE'VE ALL BEEN THERE. AFTER TEN GOOD YEARS, OR TWO, OR EIGHTEEN, SHE WALTZES OFF WITH THE METER READER. AND NOT ONLY **THIS**, BUT SHE WANTS THE CUISINART!

IT WAS **MY** GODDAMN CUISINART! MY FATHER GAVE IT TO ME!

HE GAVE IT TO **US** AS A **COUPLE**. YOU LEAVE THE COUPLE, YOU LEAVE THE CUISINART.

OBVIOUSLY, THESE WOMEN ARE SUFFERING FROM **ABREACTIVE APPLIANCE INTROJECTION SYNDROME.** LITERALLY AND FIGURATIVELY, THE CUISINART HAS **BECOME** THEIR RELATIONSHIP. UNABLE TO FACE SEPARATION, THEY CLING WITH MANIACAL FEROCITY TO THEIR REMAINING PIECE OF SHARED PROPERTY.

WHADDA **YOU** WANT WITH IT? YOU CAN'T COOK FOR **SHIT**!

IF I WANTED TO COOK FOR **SHIT**, I'D MAKE A **SOUFFLE** FOR LITTLE MISS ELECTRIC COMPANY!

THIS VULGAR DISPLAY OF VITRIOL WILL ESCALATE UNTIL THE TRAINED PROFESSIONAL INTERVENES.

BUT YOU MUST REMEMBER. PEOPLE IN THIS RAW EMOTIONAL STATE REQUIRE CAREFUL HANDLING. THEIR HEIGHTENED FEELINGS OF ABANDONMENT AND REJECTION MAKE THEM VERY VULNERABLE.

BITCH!

SLUT!

SHADDAP! I'LL TAKE THAT! IT'LL JUST ABOUT COVER MY FEE. NOW GET OUT OF HERE. YOU'RE GIVING ME A HEADACHE.

I'M SURE THEY FEEL BETTER ALREADY. WELL, I HOPE YOU'RE ALL ABLE TO **APPLY** THIS **LABOR-SAVING** TECHNIQUE TO YOUR OWN SORDID BREAKUPS. THANKS FOR SHARING! AND **BON APPETIT!**

149

on the Y front

I HOPE YOU DECIDE TO JOIN, MO. AT YOUR AGE YOU REALLY OUGHT TO THINK ABOUT STAYING IN SHAPE.

WOMEN'S LOCKER ROOM

UH-OH. THAT **SMELL!** IT'S TRIGGERING A **FLASHBACK!** I'M HEARING MY SEVENTH GRADE GYM TEACHER TELL ME I CAN'T CHANGE MY CLOTHES IN THE **TOILET STALL** ANYMORE, I HAVE TO UNDRESS IN FRONT OF ALL THE OTHER GIRLS!

Buy A Y Membership for a Friend

I ALWAYS LOVED THE ATMOSPHERE OF A LOCKER ROOM.

LOIS, WHAT ARE YOU WEARING?!

HUH?

I CAN'T BELIEVE YOU HAVE ON MEN'S UNDERWEAR! AND IN A PUBLIC PLACE! D'YOU WANT PEOPLE TO THINK YOU'RE SOME KIND OF **PERVERT?**

WANNA SEE MY MARKY MARK IMPERSONATION?

LO-IS!

LOOK, THESE ARE JUST REALLY COMFORTABLE. I'M SICK AND TIRED OF CHINTZY WOMEN'S UNDERWEAR!

LOOK! SEE HOW SHODDILY THEY'RE MADE? LOOK WHERE THE SEAM DIGS INTO YOUR WAIST, AND HOW THESE UNFINISHED LEG BANDS CHAFE YOUR SKIN

NO WAY WOULD MEN EVER WEAR SOMETHING THAT UNCOMFORTABLE! I'VE APPROPRIATED THESE JOCKEY SHORTS AS A SYMBOLIC PROTEST AGAINST THE EGREGIOUS INEQUITIES OF OUR ANDROCENTRIC CULTURE! PLUS I THINK THE STRIPE ON THE WAISTBAND IS COOL.

HUH. MAYBE YOU HAVE A POINT.

I THINK I'M MORE THE BOXER TYPE MYSELF. MAYBE A SEDATE PAISLEY PATTERN.

Cyber-dykes

HEY, GINGER! CAN I COME IN?

HI, MO! WHAT BRINGS YOU OUT ON A NIGHT LIKE THIS?

I WANTED TO FIND OUT MORE ABOUT THAT PANEL DISCUSSION TOMORROW ON LESBIAN MOTIFS IN TABLOID JOURNALISM.

OH, SURE! I WAS JUST SENDING OUT E-MAIL ANNOUNCEMENTS ABOUT IT. NOW THAT I HAVE A MODEM, I CAN HOOK UP TO THE **INTERNET** THROUGH THE UNIVERSITY.

THIS TECHNOLOGY IS INCREDIBLE! I'VE GOTTEN ADDICTED TO IT LATELY. I CAN DISCUSS SAFE SEX TIPS WITH A DYKE IN TOKYO, FIND OUT WHAT DAILY QUEER LIFE IS LIKE IN ZAGREB, LEARN ABOUT THE LATEST LESBIAN AND GAY RIGHTS DEVELOPMENTS IN SOUTH AFRICA AS SOON AS THEY HAPPEN...

AND SINCE ELECTRONIC COMMUNICATION IS CHEAPER AND FASTER THAN MAIL, THE POTENTIAL FOR GRASSROOTS ACTIVISM IS **MIND-BOGGLING!** YOU CAN NOTIFY PEOPLE ABOUT LAST-MINUTE PROTESTS AND MEETINGS, SEND DOCUMENTS, ORGANIZE E-MAIL AND FAX ZAPS! WHAT A GREAT TOOL FOR FIGHTING THE WELL-FUNDED MEDIA CAMPAIGNS OF THE **CHRISTIAN RIGHT!**

WHY? DON'T FUNDAMENTALISTS HAVE COMPUTERS TOO?

WELL, YEAH. THAT'S WHY IT'S SO IMPORTANT TO STAY ON THE CUTTING EDGE OF THE EMERGING TECHNOLOGY. YOU SHOULD REALLY THINK ABOUT BECOMING MORE COMPUTER LITERATE, MO.

YEAH, YEAH. LISTEN, IT'S PAST MY BEDTIME. COULD YOU JUST DOWNLOAD THE INFORMATION ON WHAT TIME TOMORROW'S PANEL STARTS?

OH. 7:30. SEE, MO, IF YOU WERE ONLINE, YOU WOULDN'T HAVE TO HIKE OVER HERE IN A BLIZZARD TO FIND THAT OUT.

RIGHT. AND IF YOU WERE **OFFLINE**, I COULD'VE JUST **CALLED**. YOUR PHONE'S BEEN BUSY FOR THE LAST THREE HOURS.

151

HI! AFTER YEARS OF DISASTROUS MISADVENTURES AND DEVASTATING BREAKUPS, I'VE FINALLY GOTTEN INTO AN EMOTIONALLY HEALTHY RELATIONSHIP.

ISN'T IT GREAT?

THIS VALENTINE'S SEASON, I'D LIKE TO THANK THE WONDERFUL WOMEN WHO HELPED ME TO GET WHERE I AM TODAY. AFTER ALL, IF IT WEREN'T FOR THE VALUABLE LESSONS TAUGHT ME BY MY EX-LOVERS, I'D STILL **BE** WITH THEM!

TALKING ABOUT OUR EX-LOVERS DOESN'T THREATEN OUR GENUINE INTIMACY.

BEATRICE SHOWED ME THAT IT'S FUTILE TO TRY CHANGING ANOTHER PERSON'S BEHAVIOR...

BEATRICE, IF I COULD QUIT, SO CAN YOU! THINK OF YOUR LUNGS! DO YOU HAVE SOME KIND OF DEATH WISH OR SOMETHING? BEATRICE, IF YOU DON'T QUIT, I... I'M LEAVING!

COMING TO POWER

... AND DENISE TAUGHT ME NEVER TO MAKE ASSUMPTIONS! THANKS, DENISE!

WHAT DO YOU MEAN, YOU NEVER SAID YOU WERE MONOGAMOUS?! AFTER SIX YEARS TOGETHER, I THOUGHT IT WAS SAFE TO ASSUME WE HAD AN **AGREEMENT**!

ELOISE HELPED ME TO LEARN TO EXPRESS MY OWN NEEDS.

UM... SWEETHEART? D'YOU THINK MAYBE OPHELIA COULD POSSIBLY SLEEP ON THE FLOOR JUST FOR TONIGHT?

SNORT

JANICE TAUGHT ME THAT EVERYTHING DOESN'T ALWAYS HAVE TO BE EQUAL.

OKAY. ACCORDING TO MY RECORDS, YOU CAME TWICE LAST TIME AND I ONLY CAME ONCE, SO YOU OWE ME AN ORGASM.

AND WITHOUT GWEN, I'D NEVER HAVE LEARNED THE IMPORTANCE OF HEALTHY BOUNDARIES.

YOU LOOK LIKE A GODDAMN J. CREW MODEL! YOU CAN'T GO TO THE PARTY LIKE THAT! WHAT WILL PEOPLE THINK OF ME?

SO THANKS, GIRLS! I LOVE YOU ALL AND HOPE YOU'VE EACH ENDED UP IN AS GRATIFYING AND MATURE A RELATIONSHIP AS I HAVE.

PUMPKIN, ARE YOU DONE TALKING TO THESE PEOPLE? BECAUSE SOMEONE I KNOW HASN'T DONE HER YOGA EXERCISES YET TODAY!

MOVE OVER, SUSIE BRIGHT!
GET BACK, JOANN LOULAN!
IT'S TIME FOR...

GUERILLA SEX THERAPY

WITH CLEO BALDSHEIN, M.S.W.!

HELLO, ALL YOU DISSATISFIED WOMEN! WELCOME TO TODAY'S COUPLES-ONLY WORKSHOP! WHO'S GOT A PROBLEM FOR ME?

UM...I DO, CLEO. I'VE, UH... BEEN HAVING TROUBLE ACHIEVING ORGASM WITH MY PARTNER LATELY.

IS THIS YOUR PARTNER? SOUNDS LIKE YOU NEED TO BRUSH UP ON THE OLD TECHNIQUE, EH PAL?

IT'S NOT THAT! SHE'S A WONDERFUL LOVER! AND WE HAVE A GREAT RELATIONSHIP. I DON'T KNOW WHAT THE PROBLEM IS. IN MY LAST RELATIONSHIP, WHICH WAS OTHERWISE COMPLETELY DYSFUNCTIONAL, THE SEX WAS FINE!

AH! THE SOLUTION IS SIMPLE! GO BACK TO YOUR EX! THEN MAKE SURE YOU BRING HER TO MY WEEKEND SEMINAR, "GOOD SEX, BAD RELATIONSHIP." ONLY $249 WITH THIS COUPON.

NEXT!

MY PARTNER DOESN'T FEEL LIKE MAKING LOVE VERY OFTEN, AND IT'S GOTTEN TO BE A REAL PROBLEM BETWEEN US.

PROBLEM SHMOBLEM! IF SHE WON'T HAVE SEX WITH YOU, THIS NICE WOMAN IS AVAILABLE! KNOCK YOURSELVES OUT.

AND WHAT MIGHT YOUR ISSUE BE? MY, THOSE ARE LOVELY BOOTS.

THANKS, CLEO. MY LOVER IS VERY RELUCTANT TO TRY NEW SEXUAL PRACTICES WITH ME.

LOOK, JANINE! I'M SORRY, BUT I DRAW THE LINE AT ACTING OUT YOUR SICK, MILITARISTIC FANTASIES ABOUT GOMER PYLE AND THE SERGEANT!

LIKE WHAT? GOMER GIVING SARGE'S BOOTS A SPIT SHINE?

WELL, YES, AS A MATTER OF FACT. AMONG OTHER THINGS.

SEE ME LATER.

TIME'S UP, PLEASURE-SEEKERS! I HOPE TODAY'S SESSION HAS DEEPENED BOTH THE PASSION AND THE INTIMACY OF YOUR RELATIONSHIP! BE WELL, FOLLOW YOUR BLISS, AND DON'T FORGET TO SIGN MY MAILING LIST ON YOUR WAY OUT!

153

Mama's Little Exemption

OKAY. I THINK I HAVE THIS FIGURED OUT. SINCE YOU'RE IN A HIGHER TAX BRACKET THAN I AM, WE'LL SAVE MORE MONEY IF YOU CLAIM RAFAEL AS YOUR DEPENDENT. AND I'LL FILE AS HEAD OF HOUSEHOLD, BECAUSE I CAN TAKE A LARGER STANDARD DEDUCTION THAT WAY.

"HEAD OF HOUSEHOLD." THAT'S GOT KIND OF A NICE RING, CLARICE, ARE YOU LISTENING TO ME?

BABY, YOU KNOW I HATE THAT STUFF. YOU'RE THE TAX GENIUS. DO WHATEVER YOU WANT.

WE'D SAVE EVEN MORE IF **YOU** FILED AS HEAD OF HOUSEHOLD. BUT SINCE YOU'RE NOT RAFAEL'S LEGAL MOTHER OR A BLOOD RELATIVE, YOU CAN'T.

WHAT? WAIT A MINUTE! YOU MEAN, IF, LIKE, MY BROTHER CLARENCE WAS THE SPERM DONOR, AND I WAS THEREFORE RELATED BY BLOOD TO RAFFI, WE'D PAY LESS TAXES?

MAMA SPOON!

YEAH. I THOUGHT THAT MIGHT PIQUE YOUR LEGAL INTEREST.

HUH. WE SHOULD'VE THOUGHT OF THAT THREE YEARS AGO. IT WOULD'VE BEEN FUN TO OUTFOX THE I.R.S. AT THEIR OWN GAME.

JUICE GONE.

I MEAN, WHAT BUSINESS IS IT OF THE GOVERNMENT HOW PEOPLE ARE RELATED? THEY'RE USING THE TAX CODE AS A FORM OF **SOCIAL CONTROL!** IT'S A WAY TO DISCOURAGE ALTERNATIVE FAMILIES AND REWARD HETERONUCLEAR ONES! I SAY LET'S GET THE STATE OUT OF OUR PERSONAL RELATIONSHIPS!

ACTUALLY, WE'RE PAYING LESS THIS WAY THAN IF WE WERE MARRIED AND FILING A JOINT RETURN.

OH.

RAFFI!

CHEEYOS GONE.

SPLAT

BABE, CAN YOU GET THIS ONE? I'LL BE LATE FOR MY MEETING.

HEY, HE'S YOUR DEPENDENT.

AN UNSUITABLE DISPLAY

MO'S TRUSTY OLD ONE-PIECE HAS FINALLY SPRUNG ITS ELASTIC.

NOW OUR HEROINE MUST FACE AN ORDEAL WHICH STRIKES TERROR INTO THE HEART OF FEMBOT AND FEMINIST ALIKE...

JEEZIZ! WHO'D THEY DESIGN THIS FUCKIN' THING FOR? I MEAN, WHO IN THEIR RIGHT MIND WOULD WANT TO EXPOSE THIS PART OF THEIR BODY?

IS IT TOO MUCH TO ASK FOR A SUIT THAT COVERS MY PUBIC HAIR?

HERE. THIS ONE'S CUT A LITTLE LOWER.

I HATE THIS, LOIS!

I'M A MATURE, POLITICALLY AWARE LESBIAN! I KNOW THAT FAT IS A FEMINIST ISSUE! I UNDERSTAND HOW WOMEN HAVE IMPOSSIBLE STANDARDS OF APPEARANCE SHOVED DOWN OUR THROATS! AND I LOVE MY BODY THE WAY IT IS...

UNTIL I HAVE TO BUY A GODDAMN BATHING SUIT! LOOKIT! CELLULITE, VARICOSE VEINS, PALE, FLABBY THIGHS!

JEEZ, MO! CHILL!

I KNOW! I SOUND LIKE A "CATHY" CARTOON! DON'T TELL ANYONE HOW INSECURE AND UNEVOLVED I REALLY AM, OKAY?

MO, OF COURSE YOU HAVE NEGATIVE FEELINGS ABOUT YOUR BODY! IT'S IMPOSSIBLE NOT TO IN THIS CULTURE! CUT YOURSELF SOME SLACK. YOU'RE ONLY MAKING THINGS WORSE BY EXPECTING YOURSELF TO BE PERFECTLY SELF-ACTUALIZED ABOUT IT ALL!

MAYBE YOU'RE RIGHT, LOIS. THANKS FOR PUTTING IT IN PERSPECTIVE. SO YOU HAVE THESE FEELINGS TOO?

WATCH MY STUFF, WILL YA? I'M GONNA GO TRY ON ONE OF THOSE THONGS.

LET'S JOIN MO AND LOIS FOR SOME LIFE IN THE

SLOW LANE

OUR HEROINES CLOSE UP SHOP ON A MUGGY SUMMER'S EVE.

SO YOU STILL WANNA SEE THAT MOVIE TONIGHT

YEAH. LET'S GO BY THE CO-OP AND GET SOMETHING FOR DINNER FIRST. WE SHOULD JUST MAKE THE 9:00 SHOW.

MADWIMMIN BOOKS

CLIK!

Closed

JUST DO ME

WHAT DO YOU WANNA MAKE?

JEEZ, I DUNNO. SOME KINDA SALAD?

HEY, GIRLS! HOW ABOUT TABOULI? WE JUST GOT THIS FRESH MINT IN, AND I CAN GIVE YOU A FABULOUS RECIPE.

...SO THEN ANN SAID SHE WOULDN'T COME IF SUZETTE WAS BRINGING LILA, AND...

WAIT A MINUTE! NOT LILA OF LILA AND RACHEL?

OH, MO! LILA AND RACHEL ARE HISTORY! RACHEL'S ALREADY PREGNANT WITH ANOTHER WOMAN.

EXCUSE ME, MISS. CAN YOU TELL ME WHAT THIS IS?

HERBS & SPICES

UH... YEAH. IT'S A KIND OF SEAWEED OR SOMETHING. YOU SOAK IT BEFORE YOU EAT IT. I THINK IT'S GOOD FOR YOU.

BULK HIJIKI

HUH. NO MORE RICE-NUTZ CEREAL. I'M GONNA GO BACK AND SEE IF THERE'S ANY IN THE STOREROOM.

FIBER NUGGETS

FROSTED ALFALFA

MILLET PELLETS

SOY PUFFS

CHAF

SHREDDED SPELT

KOLON KLENZ CEREAL

RAW BITS

QUINOA FLAKE

OAT FLAKE

HAY IN A BOX

HAVE YOU TWO SIGNED THIS PETITION TO STOP THE CITY FROM TURNING THE COMMUNITY GARDEN PLOTS INTO A BUCKET O' BALLS DRIVING RANGE?

COFFEE & TEA

BAGELS & BREAD

D'YOU REMEMBER HOW MUCH THIS COST?

DARN! NO, I DON'T. I'LL GO BACK AND CHECK.

GARBAGE

VEGGIE GAZETTE

CAT LITTER

ISN'T SHOPPING AT THE CO-OP GREAT? LOOK AT ALL THE MONEY WE SAVED!

VENUE CO-OP

WHADDAYA MEAN? WE COULD'VE GOTTEN SOME OF THIS STUFF CHEAPER AT MEGA-FOODS.

NO PARKIN

YEAH, BUT IT'S 8:45 ALREADY. WE JUST SAVED FIFTEEN BUCKS ON MOVIE TICKETS.

I think this comes across a little more negatively than I intended. I actually love shopping at my co-op. Most of the time.

Ever wonder if you'll see lesbian cartoon characters in the funny pages in your lifetime? Perhaps mainstream newspaper editors would be more open to the possibility if a familiar, nonthreatening format were employed. To that end, we have drawn up some sample strips which we hope will help foster a spirit of tolerance and understanding in the average comics reader.

CATHY-MO

MO AND LOIS

MO TRAIL

157

Lesbo PHOBIAS

Though lesbians as a group tend to exhibit a slightly lower incidence of phobias common to the general population (such as fears of dark places, power tools, and authority, for example), there are a few recently isolated phobias which appear to be lesbian-specific and which are here listed for your perusal and edification.

TAFFETAPHOBIA: FEAR OF BEING ASKED TO BE A BRIDESMAID IN ONE OF YOUR SISTERS' WEDDINGS.

HETEROGYNOPEEPOPHOBIA: FEAR OF STRAIGHT WOMEN THINKING YOU'RE CHECKING THEM OUT AT THE GYM.

GERALDOPRAHPHOBIA: FEAR OF LESBIAN ISSUES BEING DISCUSSED IN THE MAINSTREAM MEDIA.

CLEOPATRAPHOBIA: FEAR OF OTHER PEOPLE'S PAST-LIFE HISTORIES.

FUNDAMENTAVOYEURISMOPHOBIA: FEAR OF YOUR EXPLOITS AT THE QUEER PRIDE MARCH BEING CAPTURED IN A RELIGIOUS RIGHT PROPAGANDA VIDEO.

DORMALINGAPHOBIA: FEAR OF FALLING ASLEEP WHILE MAKING LOVE TO YOUR PARTNER.

A review in a lesbian parenting newsletter mentioned that this page elicited a rather thorny question from a child. Although most of the feedback I get about kids reading my work is from parents whose young sons and daughters are huge fans, I don't think I'd want to have to explain "dormalingaphobia" to a six-year-old.

Video Verité

Our hard-to-please housemates are on a rampage at the local video emporium.

ALL THESE MOVIES ARE ABOUT **WHITE PEOPLE**.

WHITE **MEN**. AND THEIR PENISES.

JEEZ, YOU GUYS! WHAT DID YOU EXPECT? WAS THERE A REVOLUTION SINCE THE LAST TIME YOU CAME IN HERE?

WE KNEW WHAT WE WERE GETTING INTO WHEN WE DECIDED TO RENT A MOVIE, SO QUIT WHINING AND START LOOKING.

WHAT ABOUT THIS?

OH, PLEASE. I'D RATHER WATCH BRUCE WILLIS THAN THAT COY, CRYPTO-LESBIAN CLAPTRAP.

BAGDAD CAFÉ?

SEEN IT.

FOUR TIMES.

A NICE CASTRATION ANXIETY MOVIE, PERHAPS?

OR A MAN-BEING-A-BETTER-WOMAN-THAN-A-WOMAN MOVIE?

IT MUST BE A REAL BUMMER TO BE AN ACTRESS. MEN'S ROLES OUTNUMBER WOMEN'S, LIKE, THIRTY-TO-ONE.

YEAH. THE ONLY MOVIES WITH MORE GIRLS THAN BOYS ARE IN THE PORNO SECTION.

HMM... MAYBE WE OUGHTA...

FORGET IT, LOIS. WE ARE **NOT** RENTING "AEROBISEX GIRLS" AGAIN.

Holiday Hints for Hopeless Heathens

DO GIVE YOUR PARENTS MEANINGFUL GIFTS WHICH WILL HELP FURTHER THEIR SELF-AWARE-NESS AND SPIRITUAL GROWTH.

DON'T CUT OFF THE POWER TO GARISH NATIVITY DISPLAYS AS A PROTEST AGAINST COMPULSORY CHRISTIANITY WITHOUT FOLLOWING PROPER ELECTRICAL TECHNIQUE.

DO TEACH YOUR CHILDREN TO TAKE PRIDE IN THEIR CULTURAL HERITAGE.

DON'T FORGET TO OBTAIN, IN ADVANCE, A COMPLETE LISTING OF AL-ANON MEETINGS IN THE TOWN WHERE YOU'LL BE VISITING YOUR FAMILY.

DO INSIST ON GETTING YOUR LOVER INTO THE FAMILY PHOTO!

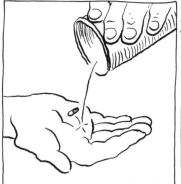

DON'T RUN OUT OF PROZAC.

DON'T UNDER ANY CIRCUMSTANCES ENTER A MALL WITHOUT BACKUP.

161

signs o' the ZODIAC to watch out for

◆ What's in the stars? ◆ Size up potential lovemates! ◆ See what cartoon celebrity shares your sign!

"TWENTY-NINE."

Lois

Aries

(MAR. 21 - APR. 19)
IMPULSIVE, CREATIVE, VOLATILE, AND PRO-MISCUOUS, ARIES BABES BELIEVE THEM-SELVES TO BE IRRESIS-TIBLY SEXY AND SOME-TIMES ACTUALLY ARE. THEY'RE QUITE RO-MANTIC, BUT IF YOU SAY YOU'D LIKE TO SPEND MORE TIME WITH THEM, THEY GET PANICKY AND FEEL LIKE THEY CAN'T BREATHE. ON THE OTHER HAND, THEY'RE NOT THE LEAST BIT POSSESSIVE. THEY ROUTINELY LIE ABOUT THEIR AGE.

"IT'S IN THE MAIL? UH-HUH."

Jezanna

Taurus

(APR. 20 - MAY 20)
GOOD-NATURED, DULL, RELIABLE, AND IN-SANELY JEALOUS. TAURIANS ARE THE SUSPICIOUS TYPE. THEY NEVER FULLY TRUST ANYONE, BUT MAYBE THAT'S WHY THEY ALWAYS SEEM TO HAVE MONEY. THEY'RE VERY KIND, BUT DON'T CROSS THEM. THEY LOVE BEING IN A RUT AND WILL BECOME ANXIOUS AND DEPRESSED IF THEIR FAVORITE SITCOM GETS MOVED TO A DIFFERENT NIGHT, OR THE LOGO ON THE MILK CARTON CHANGES.

June

Gemini

(MAY 21 - JUNE 20)
QUICK-WITTED, LIVELY, ADDICTIVE, AND GOOD WITH THEIR HANDS. GEMINIS ARE EXCELLENT LIARS AND MAKE GOOD SALESPEOPLE. THEY'RE STRANGELY ATTRACTED TO SMALL APPLIANCES AND ENJOY WATCHING LATE-NIGHT INFOMERCIALS FOR HOME EXERCISE EQUIPMENT. THEY LOVE TALKING ON THE PHONE, BUT DON'T TELL THEM ANYTHING YOU WOULDN'T WANT BROADCAST ON THE SIX O'CLOCK NEWS.

"I DON'T KNOW WHAT YOU'D DO WITHOUT ME."

Toni

Cancer

(JUNE 21 - JULY 22)
CANCERS ARE QUIET, INTUITIVE, AND LOV-ING, BUT IF ATTACKED, WILL HONE IN ON YOUR WEAK SPOT AND KICK YOU THERE VICIOUS-LY. THEY'RE DE-VOTED TO THEIR FAMILIES, AND TEND TO BE VERY FER-TILE. THEY GET OFF ON IMAGINING THAT THEY ARE INDISPENSABLE, AND HAVE HIGHLY ENMESHED RELATION-SHIPS WITH THE PEOPLE CLOSEST TO THEM. THEY ARE BIG TIGHTWADS AND BUY GENERIC BRANDS WHENEVER POSSIBLE.

"MOMMY, WIPE ME!"

Rafael

Leo

(JULY 23 - AUG. 22)
GREGARIOUS, OVER-BEARING, AND POPULAR, LEOS ARE AT THEIR BEST IN FRONT OF AN AUDIENCE. THEY'RE NOT VERY SELECTIVE ABOUT THEIR FRIENDS, AND THEY SULK IF YOU IGNORE THEM. THEY TEND TO EXCEL AT THEIR JOBS DUE TO THEIR SKILL AT CHARM-ING OTHER PEOPLE INTO DOING THEIR SHITWORK FOR THEM. THEY HAVE A DEEP-LY INGRAINED SENSE OF ENTITLEMENT AND SECRETLY WISH THEY'D BEEN BORN INTO A ROYAL FAMILY.

"YOU LEFT OUT 'CRITICAL'."

Mo

Virgo

(AUG. 23 - SEPT. 22)
DUTIFUL, SENSIBLE, AND SELF-SUFFICIENT, VIRGOS HATE BEING TOLD THAT THEY'RE FUSSY AND ANAL-RETENTIVE, BUT THEY ARE. THEY OFTEN HAVE HIGHLY SUCCESSFUL CAREERS IN PROOFREADING. SECRETLY, THEY LONG FOR THE TUMUL-TUOUS PASSION OF A NEW RELATIONSHIP TO DIE DOWN SO THEY CAN GET ON WITH THEIR WORK. ALTHOUGH THEY FANTASIZE ABOUT SEX TOYS A LOT, THEY'RE USUALLY TOO REPRESSED TO ACTUALLY GO BUY ANY.

"ON THE OTHER HAND, I SEE YOUR POINT."

Harriet

Libra

(SEPT. 23 - OCT. 22)
LIBRANS ARE TRUST-WORTHY, COMPANION-ABLE, AND PATHETIC-ALLY EAGER TO PLEASE. TERRIFIED OF BEING ALONE, THEY ALWAYS MAKE SURE THEY HAVE SOMEONE ELSE LINED UP BEFORE THEY DUMP YOU. THEY'RE EXCELLENT MEDIATORS DUE TO THEIR CRAVEN FEAR OF OPEN CONFLICT. FOR THE SAME REA-SON, THEY PREFER TO MANIPULATE PEOPLE RATHER THAN CONFRONT THEM DIRECTLY. THEY'RE SNAPPY DRESSERS WHEN THEY FINALLY MANAGE TO DECIDE WHAT TO WEAR.

"NO, OF COURSE I DON'T MIND."

Thea

Scorpio

(OCT. 23 - NOV. 21)
PURPOSEFUL, EXACTING, PASSIONATE, AND OFTEN SEXUALLY FRUSTRATED. SCORPIOS ARE VERY SECRETIVE AND TORTURED, AND CAN'T STAND IT WHEN PEOPLE DO THINGS BETTER THAN THEY DO. THEY LOVE TO BOTTLE UP THEIR FEELINGS, THEN SUR-PRISE YOU BY EXPLODING LIKE A MANIAC. THEY ARE CAPABLE OF DEEP DEVOTION, BUT IF YOU EVER HAVE A MISUNDERSTANDING WITH THEM, THEY WILL NEVER SPEAK TO YOU AGAIN. THEY KEEP THEIR KITCHEN KNIVES SHARP.

"MY DISSERTATION? OH, IT'S COMING ALONG."

Ginger

Sagittarius

(NOV. 22 - DEC. 21)
WELL-LIKED, EASILY BORED, UNRELIABLE. SAGITTARIANS HAVE LIVELY AND INQUIRING MINDS AND THEY'RE AL-WAYS COMING UP WITH CLEVER SCHEMES THAT THEY NEVER FOLLOW THROUGH ON. THEY ARE CHARMING, EXTRA-VAGANT LOVERS, BUT ONE RELATIONSHIP AT A TIME IS USUALLY NOT ENOUGH STIMULATION FOR THEM. THEY ENJOY TELLING PEOPLE WHAT TO DO AND OFTEN BECOME TEACHERS, WHICH IS TOO BAD BECAUSE THEY CAN'T EARN ENOUGH TO SUPPORT THEIR SHOCKING THRIFTLESSNESS.

"AN AFFAIR?! NO, I REALLY AM WORKING LATE!"

Clarice

Capricorn

(DEC. 22 - JAN. 20)
DETERMINED, AMBITIOUS, AND SHREWD, CAPRI-CORNS TEND TO COM-PENSATE FOR THEIR DEEPLY ROOTED IN-SECURITY BY BECOM-ING LADDER-CLIMBING WORKAHOLICS. THEY'RE GENERALLY UNDEMONSTRATIVE, BUT GOOD AT FLATTERY IF THEY THINK IT'LL GET THEM ANYWHERE. THEY'RE STEADY AND FAITHFUL LOVERS, PRIMARILY BECAUSE THEY'RE TOO BUSY TO FOOL AROUND. THEY TEND TO EXPECT THE WORST, WHICH USUALLY OBLIGES THEM BY HAPPENING.

"EVEN A SMALL CONTRIBUTION WILL HELP."

Ellen

Aquarius

(JAN. 21 - FEB. 19)
IDEALISTIC REFOR-MERS, AQUARIANS OFTEN HAVE A REALLY WEAK SENSE OF HU-MOR. THEY'RE NOT VERY AMOROUS, AND TEND TO CHANNEL THEIR PASSION INTO SAVING THE WORLD, A CAUSE WHICH THEY TAKE VERY PERSONALLY. ODDLY, THEY HAVE LITTLE PATIENCE WITH THE REAL-LIFE PROBLEMS OF THEIR FRIENDS. THEY OFTEN BECOME LEADERS BECAUSE THEY CAN'T STAND THE THOUGHT OF BEING LIKE EVERYONE ELSE. THEY MAKE FRIGHTENINGLY EFFECTIVE FUNDRAISERS.

"ACTUALLY, I'M A DOUBLE PISCES WITH A CANCER MOON."

Sparrow

Pisces

(FEB. 20 - MAR. 20)
GENTLE, CONTEMPLA-TIVE, HYPERSENSITIVE AND FLAKY. PISCEANS ARE WILDLY ROMAN-TIC AND IDEALIZE LOVE SO MUCH THAT THEIR REAL GIRLFRIENDS ARE BIG DISAPPOINT-MENTS TO THEM. THEY HATE RULES AND SYS-TEMS, WHICH IS UNFORTUNATE BECAUSE THEY OFTEN END UP BEING SOCIAL WORKERS. THEY BUY SELF-IMPROVEMENT BOOKS, AND CAN BE FOUND IN DISPROPORTIONATE NUM-BERS IN ASHRAMS, MEDITATION RETREATS, AND GET-RICH-QUICK SEMINARS.

WELCOME, ALL YOU WALKING WOUNDED, TO ANOTHER **GUERILLA THERAPY**™ WORKSHOP WITH CLEO BALDSHEIN, M.S.W.! TODAY WE WILL PONDER THAT ENDURING CONUNDRUM...

Can This Relationship Be Saved?

WELL, WELL, WELL. SO THINGS HAVEN'T BEEN GOING VERY WELL WITH THE OLE' BALL AND CHAIN LATELY, EVEN THOUGH YOU'VE BOTH BEEN WORKING HARD AT IT?

YOU NOW FACE POSSIBLY THE MOST IMPORTANT DECISION OF YOUR LIFE. DO YOU CONTINUE THE STRUGGLE, FINDING IN THE CONFLICTS AND CHALLENGES WITH YOUR PARTNER A SOURCE OF SPIRITUAL GROWTH THAT FURTHERS YOUR QUEST FOR THE TRANSCENDENT EXPERIENCE OF **TRUE INTIMACY?!**

OR DO YOU **BAIL**, AND CUT YOUR LOSSES?

THANKS TO MY EXTRAORDINARY THERAPEUTIC TECHNIQUE, I AM ABLE TO PROVIDE YOU WITH AN INSTANT ANSWER TO THIS QUESTION, SAVING YOU MONTHS, EVEN YEARS, OF PAINFUL SOUL-SEARCHING AND UGLY EMOTIONAL SHOWDOWNS. NOW, WHO CAN I HELP?

ME, CLEO! MY RELATIONSHIP HAS BECOME A **LIVING HELL.** MY PARTNER **INSISTS** THAT THE LOOSE END OF THE TOILET PAPER SHOULD HANG OVER THE **FRONT** OF THE ROLL AND NOT DOWN THE BACK AS COMMON SENSE, IF NOT GRAVITY, DICTATES. SHOULD I LEAVE HER?

ARE YOU TOYING WITH ME? I'M HERE TO SOLVE **SERIOUS** PROBLEMS, NOT TRIFLING CASES OF IRRECONCILABLE DIFFERENCES! OF COURSE YOU SHOULD LEAVE HER. **NEXT!**

CLEO, MY LOVER IS STILL IN LOVE WITH HER EX, AND WANTS HER TO COME LIVE WITH US IN A THREE-WAY RELATIONSHIP. SHOULD I GET OUT NOW, OR DO YOU THINK THIS COULD WORK?

AS LONG AS YOU HAVE MORE THAN ONE BATHROOM, GO FOR IT!

I HAVE A PROBLEM, CLEO. MY WIFE OF FIFTEEN YEARS JUST REALIZED SHE'S A BUTCH, NOT A FEMME. I'VE NEVER BEEN ATTRACTED TO OTHER BUTCHES. WHAT SHOULD I DO?

GET A BEAUTY MAKEOVER AND SOME FRILLY UNDERGARMENTS. IT WON'T HURT YOU TO FLIP-- IN FACT, IT'S BETTER FOR YOUR BACK! **NEXT!**

MS. BALDSHEIN, MY LOVER IS ALWAYS GOING ON ABOUT HOW ATTRACTIVE HER CO-WORKER IS, AND...

THAT'S NOT A CRIME! A WANDERING EYE IS THE SIGN OF A HEALTHY LIBIDO! I'M SURE YOU TWO CAN WORK THINGS OUT. **NEXT!**

BUT CLEO... YESTERDAY I FOUND A NAKED PHOTO OF THE COWORKER IN MY LOVER'S BRIEFCASE! AFTER I EXPRESSLY **FORBID** LOUISE TO EVER HAVE SEX WITH HER AGAIN!

SERVES YOU RIGHT FOR BEING SO **RIGID.** YOU NEED TO LOOSEN UP A LITTLE IF YOU WANT TO HANG ONTO LOUISE. SHE SOUNDS LIKE A CHARMING WOMAN.

TOO BAD! OUR TIME IS UP! BUT I'M HAPPY TO SEE THAT I'VE HELPED SOME OF YOU TO STOP WAFFLING AND GET ON WITH YOUR TEDIOUS LIVES. DON'T MISS MY NEXT WORKSHOP, "THE MOSH PIT OF INTIMACY." UNTIL THEN, THANKS FOR SHARING!

Limericks for Lusty Lasses

BY MISS DELILAH B. SCONE

A RESOURCEFUL YOUNG GAL, NAME OF RUBE,
AT A CRITICAL JUNCTURE, LACKED LUBE.
THE OLIVE OIL STANK,
THE TAHINI WAS RANK,
BUT SHE FOUND SOME HAIR GEL IN A TUBE.

ON THE VERGE OF LOCKJAW, KATE INQUIRED
JUST WHAT WAS IT HER LOVER DESIRED.
"WHAT YOU'RE DOING IS SWELL,"
SHE SAID. "COULDN'T YOU TELL?
I'VE COME SIXTEEN TIMES, NOW I'M TIRED."

THE BUTCH, 'NEATH HER JEANS, LIKED
TO PACK
SUMMER SQUASH FROM THE GARDEN OUT BACK.
IT ELICITED SQUEALS
FROM GIRLS IN HIGH HEELS,
AND AFTERWARD MADE A NICE SNACK.

SOME SLIPPERY WOMEN FROM FRISCO
BOUGHT THREE DOZEN LARGE CANS OF CRISCO.
STAINS WOULDN'T BE DRASTIC,
THEY PUT DOWN SOME PLASTIC,
THEN WRESTLED TILL DAWN TO BAD DISCO.

FOR A YEAR THEIR SEX LIFE HAD BEEN DEAD,
AND THEIR THERAPIST STARTED TO DREAD
THAT UNLESS MATTERS HASTENED,
HER GOOD REPUTATION
WAS LOST, SO SHE JOINED THEM IN BED.

A FORTUITOUS HOLE IN HER JEANS
PROVIDED CELESTE WITH THE MEANS
TO ENJOY A CARESS
WITH NO NEED TO UNDRESS
WHILE SHE THRILLED TO HER FAVORITE SCENES.

I was suprised to discover my aptitude for lewd doggerel. This page was so fun to write it was scary.

PLANNING TO GET HITCHED, OR KNOW SOMEONE WHO IS... BUT CAN'T FIND THE CHAPTER ON "SAME SEX WEDDING PROTOCOL" IN EMILY POST? DON'T GET YOUR TULLE IN A TWIST! THANKS TO OUR HANDY GUIDE TO

Proper Commitment Ceremony Etiquette

YOUR DEPORTMENT WILL BE BEYOND REPROACH!

DO REGISTER AT THE MOST EXCLUSIVE HARDWARE STORE IN TOWN.

RATS. LOOKS LIKE ESTHER AND CARMEN ARE GETTING THEM THE DELUXE IMPACT WRENCH.

MIGHT I SUGGEST THE HERS AND HERS MULTIPLE-SPEED ROUTERS?

KEYS CUT

DON'T FEEL OBLIGED TO ATTEND THE UNION CEREMONY OF ANYONE WHO HAS BROKEN UP WITH YOU IN THE PAST THREE MONTHS UNDER THE PRETEXT THAT SHE'S NOT READY FOR COMMITMENT.

DO ENCOURAGE A FRANK EXCHANGE OF IDEAS AMONG YOUR FRIENDS REGARDING THE IDEOLOGICAL IMPLICATIONS OF LESBIAN MARRIAGE.

IF ANYONE KNOWS OF ANY REASON WHY THIS WOMAN AND THIS WOMAN SHOULD NOT BE JOINED IN HOLY UNION, LET THEM SPEAK NOW, OR FOREVER HOLD THEIR...

2-4-6-8! DYKES SHOULD NOT ASSIMILATE!

DON'T BE AFRAID TO RECLAIM SILLY HETERO WEDDING TRADITIONS. IT'S EMPOWERING!

DON'T FORCE YOUR STRAIGHT LITTLE BROTHER TO BE A BRIDESMAID IF HE DOESN'T WANT TO.

OH, COME ON, TODD! REMEMBER THE TIME I DRESSED YOU UP IN MY PRINCESS LEIA COSTUME? NOW WASN'T THAT FUN?

C'MON TODD! YOU'LL LOOK FABULOUS!

DO CONSIDER THE FEELINGS OF YOUR MORE SQUEAMISH RELATIVES WHEN PLANNING THE SEATING ARRANGEMENT FOR THE RECEPTION.

NICE T'MEETCHA. (BELCH) WE'RE ON JANE'S RUGBY TEAM.

THUMP!

YOU WITH THE GRIDE-PTOOIE- OR THE BROOM?

CRUNCH

DO CAREFULLY MEMORIZE THE COMPLEX INTERFAITH, MULTI-CULTURAL VOWS YOU'VE SPENT THE LAST SIX MONTHS WRITING.

...AND AS RUTH SAID TO NAOMI WHEN, UM... THEY DRANK TOGETHER FROM THE, ER... KIKOMBE CUP, UH..." OH BEAUTIFUL EARTH GODDESS, WE INVOKE THE FOUR DIRECTIONS SO THAT...THAT ALL SENTIENT BEINGS MAY, UH...

PSST!

dream date

Mo IS RAINING ON THE QUEER PRIDE PARADE.

I DON'T KNOW WHY I EVEN COME TO THIS MARCH ANY MORE. LOOK IT ALL THIS **RAINBOW** CRAP. WHEN DID WE TURN FROM A POLITICAL MOVEMENT INTO A **NICHE MARKET?!**

MO, SHUT UP AND ENJOY THE BABEFLESH. JUST THINK, THE WOMAN OF YOUR DREAMS COULD BE HERE TODAY.

ZING!

LOIS, WHO **IS** THAT?! DON'T STARE!

WHAT A STRIKING PROFILE! WHAT POISE! WHAT BIG SOFT SHOULDERS CRYING OUT TO BE BITTEN!

DUNNO. NEVER SAW HER BEFORE.

I WONDER WHO SHE IS, WHAT SHE DOES... I BET SHE'S A FIREFIGHTER... OR A WILDERNESS GUIDE... OR A **VIDEO ACTIVIST!**

WHEN SHE'S NOT OFF SHOOTING AWARD-WINNING DOCUMENTARIES, WE'LL SPEND SUNDAYS IN BED, FEEDING EACH OTHER ORGANIC FRUIT AND DOING THE CROSSWORD PUZZLE...

OUR SEX LIFE WILL BE WILD AND SPONTANEOUS...

DARLING! WE'LL MISS THE PREVIEWS OF COMING ATTRACTIONS.

BUT OF COURSE OUR INTENSE INTELLECTUAL RAPPORT WILL BE JUST AS PASSIONATE... OFTEN LEADING TO WILD AND SPONTANEOUS SEX.

BUT YOU HAVEN'T TAKEN INTO ACCOUNT IRIGARAY'S THEORY OF THE FEMALE SYMBOLIC!

SWEETHEART, YOU'RE SUCH AN ESSENTIALIST! I WANT YOU.

SHE'LL MAKE SO MUCH MONEY LEADING LLAMA TREKS THAT I CAN QUIT MY JOB AND STAY HOME WRITING BESTSELLING DETECTIVE NOVELS.

DINNER'S READY, MY LOVE!

HER PARENTS ARE CHARTER MEMBERS OF **PFLAG** AND WILL EMBRACE ME LIKE THEIR OWN CHILD. THEY'LL INSIST THAT WE ACCOMPANY THEM ON THEIR ANNUAL BICYCLE TREK THROUGH THE SOUTH OF FRANCE.

SHE'LL GET EVEN HANDSOMER AS WE AGE. YOUNG LESBIANS WILL BEG US FOR THE SECRET TO OUR ENDURING HAPPINESS AND WILD, SPONTANEOUS SEX LIFE.

HEY, MO. DON'T LOOK NOW, BUT YOUR BELOVED JUST TOOK THE OTHER END OF THE LOG CABIN CLUB BANNER.

CONSERVATIVE 'N PROUD LOG CABIN C

MAYBE IF I DON'T TELL HER I BELIEVE IN A SINGLE-PAYER HEALTH CARE SYSTEM, SHE'D LET ME BITE JUST ONE SHOULDER...

167

Shameful Secrets of the Stars

Lois: TUNES IN TO THE E-Z LISTENIN' STATION ALONE IN HER CAR.

KNOCK THREE TIMES ON THE CEILING IF YOU WU-HUNT ME!

BEEP BEEP BEEP

Jezanna: ONCE, WHILE DEPRESSED, RACKED UP A $112 PHONE CALL TO DIONNE WARWICK'S PSYCHIC FRIENDS' NETWORK.

YOU HAVE A BIG, BRIGHT AURA... I SEE A LOT OF YELLOW AND BLUE... I ALSO SEE SOMETHING SURPRISING COMING TO YOU IN THE MAIL SOON... IT LOOKS LIKE A PHONE BILL...

Ginger: ASSUMES GENDER AND PREFERENCE DRAG TO ENGAGE IN ONLINE SEX WITH UNWITTING GAY MEN. SCREEN NAME : **CYBERMEAT**

9.5 INCHES. WHAT ARE YOU WEARING?

Toni: PARKS HER TENDER, IMPRESSIONABLE CHILD IN FRONT OF VIOLENT, COMMERCIAL-LADEN TV PROGRAMS JUST SO SHE CAN GET SOME TIME ALONE.

MIGHTY MORPHINE POWER RANGERS

Mo: HAS ORDERED UNDERTHINGS FROM THE INTERNATIONAL MALE CATALOG.

Clarice: TAKES PERVERSE PLEASURE IN HER FRIENDS' ROMANTIC FAILINGS.

BUCK UP, MO. SHE DIDN'T DESERVE YOU.

JEEZ, WHAT A LOSER! HOW DID I GET TO BE SO MUCH MORE STABLE AND EMOTIONALLY MATURE THAN EVERYONE I KNOW?

SNORT

Sparrow: HAS A BREAST FETISH.

... AND GIMME A BISCUIT, MASHED POTATOES, AND PLENTY OF GRAVY WITH THAT.

KFC

Harriet: DURING SLOW SESSIONS, MAKES UP DREAMS SO HER THERAPIST WON'T GET BORED.

... AND THEN THERE **YOU** WERE, ON THE STAGE, WEARING SOME KIND OF LEATHER LINGERIE AND CRACKING A **WHIP**...

Prudence ♦ an object lesson in nine stanzas

For months, Pru suspected that things were amiss from the strange taste of latex whenever they'd kiss.

When she finally caught them, a most ugly scene ensued in which damage befell a tureen.

The scoundrel not only refused to repent, but left without paying her share of the rent.

Bereft, Pru ate nothing but stale marzipan, and thrashed about tragically on the divan.

At length, when she summoned the strength to go out, the sight of them tangoing dealt a cruel clout.

She managed to stifle a primitive urge to puncture their tires (she was just on the verge.)

Instead she determined to polish her prose, learn Latin, and get a nice ring in her nose.

She swore that she never would have sex again. It only wreaked havoc. Perhaps she'd try Zen.

But there she met Lou with the cunning tattoo, and embarked on the whole vicious circle anew.

VEGETARIAN

VEGAN

MACROBIOTIC

LOW-SODIUM

TAKE-OUT

NO WHEAT, CORN, OR SOY

NOTHING PROCESSED OR REFINED

ALLERGIC TO ROOT VEGETABLES

NOTHING GREEN

"VEGETARIAN" WHO EATS FISH

FISH WHO EATS VEGETARIANS

NOTHING COOKED

NOTHING BUT TOMATO SANDWICHES

ANYTHING THAT MOVES

HELOISE C. BLAND'S HELPFUL HOUSEHOLD HINTS SERIES PRESENTS...
the Finicky Lesbian's Guide to Dietary Substitutions

recovering chocaholic?

TO TAKE THE EDGE OFF THOSE WITHDRAWAL SYMPTOMS, TRY THIS SIMPLE TRICK!

FIND YOUR FAVORITE FUDGE RECIPE, SUBSTITUTE CAROB POWDER AND BLACKSTRAP MOLASSES FOR THE COCOA AND SUGAR, THEN **EAT THE WHOLE BATCH!** YOUR CRAVING WILL MAGICALLY DISAPPEAR!

a sensual delight

DO YOU LONG FOR YOUR GIRLFRIEND TO LICK WHIPPED CREAM FROM CERTAIN OF YOUR EROGENOUS ZONES, BUT SHE **DOESN'T DO DAIRY?**

TOSS SOME **TOFU** IN THE BLENDER! IT WHIPS UP BEAUTIFULLY, AND DOESN'T TASTE THAT BAD IF YOU ADD LOTS OF HONEY AND HOLD YOUR NOSE!

miss your Bubbe's latkes?

IF YOU'VE GIVEN UP EGGS, YOU'RE PROBABLY HAVING A HARD TIME GETTING YOUR POTATO PANCAKES TO STICK TOGETHER PROPERLY.

TRY ADDING A TABLESPOONFUL OF ELMER'S GLUE! IT'S NON-TOXIC AND HAS NO HARMFUL FUMES!

Allergic to Wheat?

... BUT YOU NEED TO **CARBO LOAD** FOR THE BIG MARATHON TOMORROW? FOUR CASES OF RICE CAKES WILL PROVIDE YOU WITH THE CARBOHYDRATE EQUIVALENT OF TWO GENEROUS HELPINGS OF PASTA!

hearty vegan fritters

LONG FOR THAT SATIATED, CONGEALED FEELING YOU USED TO GET FROM A PLATE OF MIXED GRILL, OR HALF-A-DOZEN CHEESE BLINTZES WITH SOUR CREAM?

DEEP FRY LUSCIOUS GOBS OF PEANUT BUTTER IN CANOLA OIL, ROLL IN CHOPPED MACADAMIA NUTS, AND TOP WITH A HEFTY DOLLOP OF GUACAMOLE! YUM!

you love the java jive...

BUT IT'S KILLING YOU? SURE, IT MIGHT BE NICE NOT TO HAVE HEART PALPITATIONS AND PAINFUL LUMPS IN YOUR BREASTS... BUT HOW WOULD YOU SHAKE YOUR MORNING SLUGGISHNESS WITHOUT THAT MUG OF COLOMBIAN SUPREMO?

TRY A **BREAKFAST JOLT!**
COMBINE ½ C. BEET JUICE
        ½ C. PRUNE JUICE
ADD   1 TBLSP. CAYENNE PEPPER
        4 CLOVES GARLIC, MINCED
ZAP IN MICROWAVE, AND DRINK!
YOU'LL BE ALL SYSTEMS GO IN NO TIME!

the Family Tub

EVER WONDER HOW YOUR LIFE WOULD'VE BEEN DIFFERENT IF YOU WERE BORN MALE AND HETEROSEXUAL? LET'S TAKE A LOOK AT SOME

Guys To Watch Out For

Ginger

MY COMPUTER CRASHED, MS. JORDAN, SO I HAD TO WRITE MY PAPER BY HAND. HOPE YOU CAN MAKE OUT MY CHICKENSCRATCH.

I'M NEVER GONNA FINISH MY DISSERTATION.

HOW'S YOUR DISSERTATION GOING, MR. JORDAN? NEED ME TO DO ANY MORE TYPING FOR YOU?

WHY THANK YOU, LA SHAUNA. THAT WOULD BE A BIG HELP.

Lois

CAN I TRY ON THE 'JEFF STRYKER'?

ON, YES. IN, NO.

FRY IN HELL PURVURTS

SINNERS REPENT

PRIDE '97

JESUS HATES YOU!

Clarice

...AND FOR HER PRECEDENT-SETTING WORK AGAINST THE ENVIRONMENTAL RACISM OF THE UNION CARBUNCLE COR-PORATION, THE YOUNG LAWYER OF THE YEAR AWARD GOES TO CLARICE CLIFFORD!

WHAT'RE YOU IN FOR, MAN?

DRIVING WITH AN EXPIRED INSPECTION STICKER. I GOT PULLED OVER 12 YEARS AGO ON MY WAY TO TAKE THE LSATS.

Toni

WE'LL GO TO THE PARK AND PLAY BALL AFTER MOMMY FINISHES THE DISHES AND THE LAUNDRY AND THE SHOPPING AND THE YARD-WORK AND CHANGES THE OIL IN THE CAR...

...AND FOR HIS PATIENT COACHING ALL THOSE SATURDAY AFTERNOONS, THE TOTS' TEE BALL LEAGUE IS PROUD TO PRESENT THE FATHER OF THE YEAR AWARD TO TONY ORTIZ!

Harriet

GEORGE, MY WORKLOAD HAS TRIPLED IN THE LAST YEAR. I CAN'T MANAGE THESE CASES WITHOUT SOME HELP!

HIRE YOU AN ASSISTANT? ON OUR BUDGET? YOU'VE GOTTA BE KIDDING!

Mo

HOW CAN I GO ON LIVING IN A COUNTRY WHERE **CEO**s MAKE 200 TIMES WHAT THE AVERAGE WORKER DOES? WHERE THE N.R.A. AND THE CHRISTIAN COALITION MAKE **POLICY**? WHERE WOMEN AND CHILDREN LIVE IN **SQUALOR** SO BIG CORPORATIONS CAN GET A **TAX BREAK**! I'M **ASHAMED** TO BE AN **AMERICAN**!

...AND WILL TO THE BEST OF MY ABILITY PRESERVE, PROTECT, AND DEFEND THE CONSTITUTION OF THE UNITED STATES.

Valentines for the modern lesbian

-------- ✂ CLIP-N-SEND!

TO YOUR CHIROPRACTOR

CRUNCH!

You LISTEN TO MY LAUNDRY LIST
OF AILMENTS, THEN YOU CRACK AND TWIST
WITH ABLE HANDS MY BACK AND WRIST.
IN MY DREAMS, WE'VE OFTEN KISSED.

You LOOSEN ME WHEN I AM RUSTED,
EASE MY PAIN WHEN SOMETHING'S BUSTED.
WHO CAN WONDER THAT I'VE LUSTED
FOR A GAL SO WELL-ADJUSTED?

TO YOUR BEST FRIEND

I MET YOU WHEN YOU WERE A RAW JUNIOR DYKE.
YOU KNEW I WAS QUEER BEFORE I DID.
AS LOVERS HAVE COME AND AS LOVERS HAVE GONE,
TO EACH OTHER WE'VE CRIED AND CONFIDED.

FOR NIGH ON TWO DECADES OUR BOND HAS ENDURED.
THROUGH THICK AND THROUGH THIN WE HAVE STAYED.
IF ONLY OUR GIRLFRIENDS WOULD LAST HALF AS LONG,
THEN, MY FRIEND, WE WOULD BOTH HAVE IT MADE.

I KNOW WHAT I'D SAY IN CASE ANYONE ASKS,
"TO WHAT DO YOU OWE YOUR SUCCESS?"
"TO TRUST AND TRUE LOVE," I'D REPLY WITH A SMILE.
"PLUS THE FACT THAT WE'VE NEVER HAD SEX."

TO THE WOMAN YOUR LOVER LEFT YOU FOR

SHE'S ALL YOURS NOW, YOU SHAMELESS WENCH,
I KNOW WHEN I'VE BEEN BESTED.
BUT PERHAPS NOW THAT YOUR LUST IS QUENCHED,
HER FLAWS HAVE MANIFESTED.

HER RAMPANT INSECURITY,
HER TASTE FOR RUNNY YOLKS,
HER PECULIAR INABILITY
TO COME OUT TO HER FOLKS.

IN FACT, NOW THAT I TAKE THIS VIEW,
YOU'VE DONE ME A BIG FAVOR.
BUT STILL, THE MOMENT SHE DUMPS YOU
IS ONE THAT I WILL SAVOR.

TO YOUR SPERM DONOR

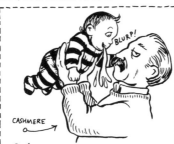

BLURP!

CASHMERE

VALENTINE, YOU WIN THE PRIZE
FOR PATIENCE, LO THESE SIXTEEN TRIES.
SERVING UP THAT VITAL FLUID,
WHETHER OR NOT YOU'RE IN THE MOO-ID.

(WITHOUT YOU, IT'S QUITE SAFE TO BET
WE'D BE TWENTY THOU IN DEBT.)

BUT WON'T IT ALL BE WORTH IT WHEN,
IN A YEAR, OR TWO, OR TEN,
A WINSOME, DROOLING LASS OR LADDIE
CALLS TO YOU, "YO! UNCLE DADDY!"

TO YOUR THERAPIST

⊙ VALENTINE, WITHOUT YOU
I'D FOR CERTAIN BE A WRECK.
I DON'T REGRET ONE PENNY
OF YOUR HEFTY WEEKLY CHECK.

MY FAMILY AND FRIENDS CAN'T
UNDERSTAND THE REAL ME
LIKE YOU DO EVERY THURSDAY
'TWIXT THE HOURS OF TWO AND THREE.

MY GIRLFRIEND TELLS ME I SHOULD QUIT,
BUT STEADFASTLY, I THWART HER.
DON'T CURE ME OR I'LL JUST CONCOCT
A NEW AND WORSE DISORDER.

I CAN'T LEAVE! I'VE BEEN
FEELING SO, UM... INADEQUATE AND,
UH... OBSESSIVE-COMPULSIVE
LATELY!

173

CLASS conscious

Mo's on her lunch break at Madwimmin Books...

PROMOTIONS, PH. D'S, PULITZERS... I'M **PATHETIC!**

?

ALL MY CLASSMATES ARE SUCCESSFUL AND ACCOMPLISHED, AND I'M STANDING AROUND TELLING PEOPLE WHICH SHELF THE LATEST EROTICA ANTHOLOGY IS ON, AND CRANKING OUT BOOK REVIEWS FOR THE LOCAL BAR RAG!

OH, NO. NOT ANOTHER ISSUE OF YOUR ALUMNI MAGAZINE. LAST TIME YOU SWORE YOU WOULDN'T DO THIS TO YOURSELF AGAIN.

RRRRRRRR

CLEAN UP AFTER YISSELF

GEN'L ATOMIC

I CAN'T HELP IT! IT'S A MORBID FIXATION. LISTEN TO THIS! THE WASTOID WHO LIVED ACROSS THE HALL FROM ME IS AN ASSOCIATE PROFESSOR OF PSYCHOPHARMACOLOGY AT STANFORD, AND HIS GEEK ROOMMATE JUST BECAME A GAZILLIONAIRE WHEN HIS COMPUTER GAME COMPANY WENT PUBLIC!

DING!

...AND THIS DITZ FROM MY FRENCH CLASS JUST MADE PARTNER AT A HUGE LAW FIRM WHILE SOMEHOW ALSO MANAGING TO REMODEL A HOUSE WITH MR. RIGHT AND RAISE THEIR THREE 'EXCEPTIONAL' CHILDREN IN HER SPARE TIME.

MO, WHY DO YOU COMPARE YOURSELF TO THESE PEOPLE? YOU DON'T WANT KIDS, OR SOME AWFUL CORPORATE JOB.

BESIDES, IT'S ONLY THE INSECURE JERKS WHO BOTHER SENDING THAT STUFF IN, AND HALF OF THEM ARE EXAGGERATING WILDLY.

FOR EXAMPLE, WANNA BET MISTER "I'VE BEEN RESEARCHING THE BIODIVERSITY OF COASTAL RAINFORESTS IN COSTA RICA FOR THE PAST YEAR" IS GETTING BANKROLLED BY HIS DAD TO BUM AROUND IN A KAYAK? AND YOU KNOW ANYONE CALLING THEMSELVES A **CONSULTANT** IS ONLY MARGINALLY EMPLOYED AT BEST.

CHECK THIS BABE OUT. "IN ADDITION TO MY WORK AS CUSTOMER RELATIONS CONSULTANT TO AN INDEPENDENT BOOKSELLER, I'M FINDING TIME TO PURSUE AN EXCITING AND SUCCESSFUL SECOND CAREER AS A LITERARY CRITIC. I MEAN, GET REAL! THAT COULD BE YOU!

ACME U. ALUMNI BULLETIN

OH. IT **IS** YOU.

I JUST DID IT FOR A JOKE.

YEAH, RIGHT. Y'KNOW, YOU **ARE** PATHETIC.

Questionable Tips for Queer Parents

A Querulous Quodlibet
by
Chloe B. de Snail, Ph.D.

Do BE SUPPORTIVE OF YOUR CHILD'S SOMETIMES AWKWARD CURIOSITY ABOUT HER ORIGINS.

IS THAT MY DADDY?

EXCUSE ME. WERE YOU BY ANY CHANCE A DEPOSITOR WITH ACME REPRODUCTIVE SERVICES BETWEEN THE YEARS OF 1990 AND 1992?

ATM

Don't TRY TOO HARD TO WIN OVER YOUR NEW LOVER'S TEENAGER.

HEY, TIGER! I GOT YOU THE NEW HOOTIE AND THE BLOWFISH ALBUM!

RANCID

Do FEEL FREE TO CONCOCT EXTRAVAGANT LIES IN RESPONSE TO TIRESOME QUESTIONS FROM CLUELESS STRANGERS.

ISN'T THAT SWEET! MOMMY'S DAY OFF?

NO. MOMMY'S IN PRISON FOR KNOCKING OVER A PAWN SHOP, BUT WE'VE MANAGED TO PICK UP THE PIECES AND MOVE ON WITH OUR LIVES.

TOX

Don't TRY TO LIVE VICARIOUSLY THROUGH YOUR CHILD.

TRAINS SUCK!

NO THEY DON'T, SUGARPLUM! LOOK AT THIS HANDSOME ENGINEER'S CAP MOMMY GOT YOU! JUST FIVE MINUTES? PLEASE?

Do FIND ROLE MODELS OF A DIFFERENT GENDER TO PROVIDE A WELL-ROUNDED EXPERIENCE FOR YOUR CHILD.

LOOK, UNCLE EUGENE. SHE'S GOING TO THE PWOM.

HMM. THE DRESS WORKS, BUT WE'RE GONNA HAVE TO DO SOMETHING ABOUT THAT HAIR.

BARBIE

Do BRING YOUR CHILDREN UP IN AN ENVIRONMENT FREE OF GENDER STEREOTYPES, UNHEALTHY EATING HABITS, AND RAMPANT CONSUMERISM.

AREN'T THOSE UNSWEETENED BRAN MUFFINS WHOLESOME, KIDS?

WHEN YOU'RE ALL DONE, MOMMY JEAN WILL MAKE HOMEMADE PLAY-DOH FOR HER BIG STRONG CHRIS AND HER SWEET, SENSITIVE ROBIN!

FREE TO BE YOU & ME

Don't DESPAIR WHEN YOU REALIZE ALL YOUR EFFORTS WERE UTTERLY FUTILE.

MOM! ROB HOGGED THE LAST HO-HO! I WAS SAVING IT FOR AFTER CHEERLEADING PRACTICE!

I DID NOT! SHUT UP, CHRISSY, OR I'LL LINE THE GERBIL CAGE WITH YOUR POM-POMS AGAIN.

I ATE THE HO-HO CHRISSY. IF YOU'RE HUNGRY, GO NUKE A BURRITO.

IRON MAID

TOUGH LOV

VISA

JEAN, WHAT'S THIS $900 CHARGE TO THE GAP? I THOUGHT YOU SAID YOU BOUGHT THEIR SCHOOL CLOTHES AT K-MART.

LESBIAN AND GAY JOURNALISM HAS COME A LONG WAY SINCE THE FIRST ISSUES OF "ONE" AND "THE LADDER" ROLLED OFF THE MIMEOGRAPH MACHINES BACK IN THE FIFTIES...

NOW WE HAVE THE QUEER VANITY FAIR...

Out
FASHION
PERFUME ADS
PLUS OBSEQUIOUS FAWNING ON STRAIGHT CELEBRITIES WHO THINK GAY IS A-OK

THE GAY NEWS-WEEK..

The Advocate
NEWS
POLITICS
A TOKEN LESBIAN
PLUS SOME STRAIGHT CELEBS WHO THINK GAY IS A-OK

AND THE LESBIAN PLAY-BOY.

GiRL FRIENDS
SOME NEWS
A REVIEW
A POEM
AND NOT MUCH ELSE CAUSE WE BLEW OUR BUDGET ON THE CENTERFOLD

WHERE WILL THIS SLICK, FOUR-COLOR JUGGERNAUT END? CAN HOMOSEX VERSIONS OF OTHER NEWSSTAND REGULARS BE FAR OFF?

Queer GLOSSIES Of The Future

CONSUMER REPORTS

BUY ▾ OUT $

how good is your SPERM BANK?

PERSONAL LUBRICANTS: WHICH WORK BEST FOR YOUR SPECIFIC NEEDS?

ALERT! DOLCE & GABBANA RECALL JEANS AFTER INJURIES REPORTED

FAST FOOD CHAINS PESTO HUT RATES HIGHEST FOR GAY FRIENDLINESS

25 CITY GUIDE TO PRIDE MARCHES WHERE TO FIND
• TRANSGENDER INCLUSIVITY
• THE BUFFEST BEEFCAKE
• THE BADDEST DYKES ON BIKES

'97 PORN VIDEO REVIEW

CAR AND DRIVER

OUT ON THE ROAD

"I HAD AN UNNATURAL RELATIONSHIP WITH MY SPORT-UTILITY VEHICLE!" —ONE BUTCH'S SHOCKING CONFESSION

A DAY AT THE DRAG RACES WITH RU PAUL

COMPARISON TESTS BMW 328i VS. INFINITI I30 WHICH TURNS MORE BOYS' HEADS? FORD EXPLORER VS. NISSAN PATHFINDER WHICH IS THE BIGGER BABE MAGNET?

RECONCILING A LUXURY CAR WITH YOUR SOCIAL CONSCIENCE

FAMILY CIRCLE

alternative FamilyCircle

HALLOWEEN SPECIAL! 6 OUTRAGEOUS COSTUME IDEAS (AND 3 FOR YOUR KIDS!)

UPDATE: HEATHER'S TWO MOMMIES IN HEATED CUSTODY BATTLE

TAKING OVER YOUR LOCAL SCHOOL BOARD IN 10 E-Z STEPS!

LESBIAN BED DEATH: TWO MOMS' TRAGIC TALE

QUICK TRICKS WITH LEFTOVER LENTILS!

DOG FANCY

FANCYDOG

MATCHING BREED TO DECOR: DOES YOUR ROTTWEILER CLASH WITH THE LOUIS QUINZE?

EXPENSIVE PET JEWELRY **OUTRAGE? OR OUTRAGEOUS!**

LESBIAN LHASA APSO? GAY GREYHOUND?

WHEN DOGS WON'T MATE

PAUNCHY POOCH TIGHTER ABS FOR YOUR PET IN 30 DAYS

TRAIN YOUR **NEAPOLITAN MASTIFF** TO SNIFF OUT HOMOPHOBES!

NATIONAL GEOGRAPHIC

subscribe now!

SPECIAL MAP SUPPLEMENT: LESBOS, 600 B.C.E.

OUTLANDISH

PARTHENOGENETIC PERFECTION OBSERVING THE WHIPTAIL LIZARD

HOMO HOMO SAPIENS? STARTLING NEW EVIDENCE

FRONTIER QUEENS "SITUATIONAL" HOMO-SEXUALITY OR TRUE LOVE AMONG THE COWBOYS

BIODIVERSITY IN SOUTH BEACH

Mardi Gras! PLUS NAKED PEOPLE THE WORLD OVER

Mo's Work-out!

Been meaning to get in shape? Here's a well-rounded conditioning program for everyone!

WARM UP (AND SAVE VALUABLE TIME!) WITH A BRISK JOG TO THE GYM.

DAMMIT! WHY'D I TELL LOIS I'D WORK LATE FOR HER? ALL THE @★#@★ STAIRMASTERS WILL BE TAKEN BY NOW!

RELIEVE STRESS AND PREVENT INJURY WITH A THOROUGH **STRETCHING** ROUTINE.

'SCUSE ME. OOPS. PARDON.

DON'T GET IN A RUT WITH A PARTICULAR PIECE OF EXERCISE EQUIPMENT. IT'S GOOD TO VARY YOUR WORKOUT.

SIGN-UP FOR MACHINES
STAIRMASTERS — ALL TAKEN
BIKES — FULL
ROWERS — S.R.O.
TREADMILLS — BOOKED THRU FRIDAY!

WELL... I GUESS I COULD GIVE THIS THING A TRY.

GET YOUR HEART RATE UP WITH TWENTY OR THIRTY MINUTES OF **AEROBIC ACTIVITY.** AS YOUR FITNESS LEVEL IMPROVES, YOU'LL EXPERIENCE A MEDITATIVE, ENDORPHIN-INDUCED EUPHORIA!

@★#★🐟!

GRIND CLANK!

WAIT TRAINING IS A CRUCIAL PART OF ANY EXERCISE REGIMEN, AND IF DONE PROPERLY, WILL ALSO INCREASE YOUR FLEXIBILITY AND ENDURANCE. DON'T QUIT NOW! YOU'RE ALMOST DONE!

NAUTILUS CIRCUIT LINE FORMS HERE

LEG RACK

MAYBE I SHOULD JUST DO SOME PUSH-UPS INSTEAD. OH, FUCK IT. I'M GONNA GO TAKE A SAUNA.

CHECK YOUR **PULSE RATE!** (COUNT HOW MANY BEATS IN SIX SECONDS, MULTIPLY BY TEN AND DIVIDE BY THE BINOMIAL COEFFICIENT OF WHAT DAY IT IS IN YOUR MENSTRUAL CYCLE.) IS IT OVER 200? CAREFUL! DON'T THROW A ROD OR ANYTHING!

DIDJA KNOW ISABEL'S SEEING THAT WOMAN WHO WORKS AT THE BOOKSTORE?

REALLY? THE CUTE ONE?

NO, THE ONE WITH THE STRIPED SHIRT AND GLASSES.

THUMP THUMPA THUMP!

DON'T FORGET TO **COOL DOWN!**

THERE'S NEVER ANY HOT WATER LEFT THIS LATE. IT'S NOT SO BAD ONCE YOU GET USED TO IT.

AAUGH!

S'PLOOSH

GIRLJOCK

THERE! DON'T YOU FEEL RELAXED AND REJUVENATED? MO'S WORKOUT IS YOUR KEY TO A NEW, HEALTHIER LIFESTYLE!

DAMMIT! I ONLY HAVE FIVE MINUTES TO GET SOMETHING HIGH IN SATURATED FAT BEFORE THE MEXICAN TAKEOUT PLACE CLOSES!

179

COSMO LOGIC DEPT. ⑥VER THE CENTURIES, WOMEN OF SAPPHIC PREDILECTIONS HAVE GAINED A REPUTATION FOR BEING UNUSUALLY TALENTED AND SENSUAL LOVERS. FROM THE AMAZONS, TO THE HAREMS OF THE PERSIAN EMPIRE, TO EVERY OTHER ADULT VIDEO ON THE MARKET, LEGENDS OF OUR PROWESS ABOUND. ARE YOU RESTING ON YOUR LESBIAN LAURELS, OR DO YOU HAVE WHAT IT TAKES TO BE A WOMYN-LOVIN'-WOMAN? FIND OUT NOW WITH OUR CAREFULLY FORMULATED QUIZ,...

how good in the sack are you?

1. HOW DO YOU INITIATE SEX WITH YOUR PARTNER?

A.) THERE'S NO NEED TO INITIATE. YOU AUTOMATICALLY DO IT EVERY SIXTH SATURDAY, RIGHT AFTER "DR. QUINN, MEDICINE WOMAN"
B.) OFFERING HER A BACKRUB
C.) GREETING HER AT THE DOOR IN A PROVOCATIVE COSTUME
D.) POPPING IN A "HOT AND HUNG" VIDEO AND DONNING YOUR STATE TROOPER UNIFORM

IS THAT A LAVENDER ZUCCHINI, OR ARE YOU JUST HAPPY TO SEE ME?

2. BEFORE GOING FOR THE GOLD, YOU GET YOUR LOVER IN THE MOOD BY...

A.) DROOLING IN HER EAR
B.) SUCKING DELICATELY ON HER TOES
C.) TEASING HER INNER THIGHS WITH A PEACOCK FEATHER
D.) RIGGING HER UP IN AN ELABORATE JAPANESE ROPE BONDAGE TECHNIQUE AND GOING OUT TO A MOVIE

DON'T GO ANYWHERE. I'LL BE RIGHT BACK AFTER **GONE WITH THE WIND.**

3. TO STIMULATE YOUR LOVER'S G-SPOT, YOU USE:

A.) UH... DO YOU MEAN THAT MOLE ON HER GROIN?
B.) FINGERS
C.) A VIBRATOR WITH A SPECIAL ATTACHMENT
D.) YOUR TONGUE

IS **THAT** IT?

JEEZIZ, LUCINDA! I'VE HAD MORE ROMANTIC PELVIC EXAMS.

4. WHAT SEXUAL RISKS HAVE YOU TAKEN LATELY?

A.) SHARED WITH YOUR LOVER YOUR FANTASY OF SLOW-DANCING WITH ELLEN DE GENERES
B.) ORDERED FLAVORED MASSAGE OIL FROM THE **GOOD VIBRATIONS** CATALOG USING YOUR REAL NAME
C.) SHARED WITH YOUR LOVER YOUR FANTASY OF BEING BRAD PITT SLOW-DANCING WITH MELISSA ETHERIDGE
D.) GOT FISTED BY A COMPLETE STRANGER ON HER HARLEY WHILE DOING 90 ON THE INTERSTATE

OKAY, OKAY. BUT CAN'T 1 BE BRAD?

NO WAY! IT'S MY FANTASY.

MELISSA.

5. YOU TYPICALLY BRING YOUR SEX PARTNERS TO SUCH HEIGHTS OF ECSTASY THAT:

A.) THEY START EXPERIMENTING WITH MEN
B.) THEIR MENSTRUAL CRAMPS SUBSIDE MOMENTARILY
C.) YOU'VE HAD TO SPECIALLY SOUNDPROOF YOUR BOUDOIR
D.) THEY BLACK OUT FROM THE SHEER FORCE OF THEIR CLIMAX

HOW WAS IT FOR YOU?

GREAT. COULD YOU GO GET ME A COUPLE ADVILS?

scoring

ADD UP YOUR POINTS! A=0, B=1, C=2, AND D=3.

0-3 YOU'RE A BLOT ON THE SAPPHIC ESCUTCHEON! BACK TO WOMEN'S STUDIES WITH YOU! AND THIS TIME, TAKE NOTES!

4-8 CLOSE, BUT NO CIGAR. NO LAVENDER ZUCCHINI, EITHER.

9-12 MUFFDIVER SUMMA CUM LOUDLY

13-15 GOOD LORD! IF YOU DON'T ALREADY, HAVE YOU CONSIDERED CHARGING?

Panel 1:

ARE YOU TENSE? IRRITABLE? OVERWORKED? DEVELOPING AN ULCER, MAYBE? WELL **RELAX** ALREADY! IT'S TIME FOR

Guerilla® Stress Management

WITH THAT PUGILISTIC PIONEER OF GUERILLA® THERAPY,...

CLEO BALDSHEIN, M.S.W.

I HAVE A MASTER'S DEGREE! IN SOCIAL WORK!

Panel 2:

HELLO, ALL YOU NERVOUS WRECKS! SINCE MUCH OF THE STRESS IN OUR LIVES IS CAUSED BY OVERCOMMITMENT, THE FIRST THING WE'RE GOING TO LEARN IS HOW TO SAY **NO**. MAKE TIME TO RELAX BY SAYING **NO** TO FAVORS, **NO** TO SPECIAL PROJECTS, **NO** TO UNNECESSARY SOCIAL INTERACTION, **NO** TO SEX...

Panel 3:

...OOPS. SCRATCH THAT LAST ONE. THAT'S FROM MY GUERILLA® SEX ADDICTION RECOVERY WORKSHOP. JUST $299 WITH YOUR RECEIPT FROM TODAY'S SEMINAR.

Panel 4:

NOW, LET'S PRACTICE SAYING **NO**. YOUR BEST FRIEND CALLS YOU AND ASKS IF YOU CAN WATER HER PLANTS WHILE SHE'S IN THE HOSPITAL FOR A KIDNEY TRANSPLANT. WHAT DO YOU SAY?

Panel 5:

UH... NO?

THAT'S RIGHT! WHAT A HEALTHILY SELFISH RESPONSE! MY EARLIER SESSION WAS FULL OF CODEPENDENT BLEEDING HEARTS. NOW, ANOTHER GREAT WAY TO REDUCE STRESS IS TO AVOID PROCRASTINATION. ANY PROCRASTINATORS HERE TODAY?

Panel 6:

YES, CLEO! I'M ALWAYS PUTTING THINGS OFF TILL THE LAST POSSIBLE MINUTE, THEN WORKING LIKE A MANIAC TO GET THEM DONE. AS A RESULT, I'M CONSTANTLY **STRESSED OUT**.

Panel 7:

THEN **STOP** IT! I HAVE ABSOLUTELY NO PATIENCE WITH PEOPLE LIKE YOU! WHAT'S THE BIG DEAL? YOU HAVE SOMETHING TO DO? **JUST DO IT!**

SAY, THAT'S RATHER CATCHY.

Panel 8:

MEMO: MERCHANDISING IDEA: "JUST DO IT" T-SHIRTS.

Panel 9:

CLEO, NONE OF YOUR ADVICE SO FAR APPLIES TO MY SITUATION. I'VE BEEN UNDER A GREAT DEAL OF STRAIN LATELY SINCE MY LOVER LEFT ME, I GOT DOWNSIZED OUT OF A JOB, MY ALCOHOLIC BROTHER MOVED IN WITH ME, MY HOUSE WAS VANDALIZED, AND MY EX-HUSBAND WON CUSTODY OF MY DAUGHTER. ANY TIPS ON HOW I CAN MANAGE MY STRESS?

Panel 10:

DO SOMETHING TO IMPROVE YOUR APPEARANCE! A HAIRCUT, SOME NEW CLOTHES. **LOOKING** BETTER CAN HELP YOU **FEEL** BETTER.

Panel 11:

...AND IT COULDN'T HURT TO WORK ON THAT ATTITUDE! INSTEAD OF FOCUSING ON YOUR OWN PETTY PROBLEMS, DO SOMETHING FOR SOMEONE ELSE! I COULD USE SOME HELP WITH MY BILLING AND INSURANCE PAPERWORK.

BUT CLEO, WOULDN'T THAT CONTRADICT YOUR EARLIER ADVICE TO JUST SAY NO?

PUNCH!

Panel 12:

OH, WHAT A SHAME! WE'RE ALL OUT OF TIME! LET'S END WITH AN ANCIENT YOGIC DEEP-BREATHING PRACTICE.

IN!

Panel 13:

AND **OUT!** THERE! DIDN'T ALL THAT TENSION JUST MELT AWAY? TA-TA, AND ENJOY YOUR NEW LIFE IN THE SLOW LANE!

ON YOUR WAY OUT, PICK UP MY "DON'T FORGET TO BREATHE" T-SHIRT, SPECIALLY PRICED AT JUST $29.99.

You've been out to your family for years. They've been through the shock, the denial, the grief, and the acceptance. But do they accept you as an equal? Or do they accept you the way they would, say, a root canal? Maybe one day they'll finally get beyond...

those old Double Standards

RESPECT FOR A COMMITTED RELATIONSHIP

SUPPORT FOR A BREAKUP

PUBLIC DISPLAYS OF AFFECTION

ACCEPTANCE OF NEW FAMILY MEMBERS

TALKING ABOUT YOUR PARTNER

TALKING TO YOUR PARTNER

Chapter Five
Commissions and Collaborations

Original version

Writing and illustrating your own comic strip is an ideal job for rugged individualists and other people with control issues. I get to be screenwriter, producer, director, complete cast, dialogue coach, set designer, property master, costumer, title designer, camera operator, editor, production supervisor, accountant, caterer, animal wrangler, and key grip for my own little dramas. My girlfriend gives me invaluable editorial assistance, and I get material from various readers, friends, and research consultants. But for the most part, I work alone and like it that way.

I savor my freedom, especially when I hear tales of the Machiavellian workplace politics that most of my friends have to put up with. No syndicate executive tells me what topics I should or shouldn't write about. I don't have to run my work by anyone's approval before sending it out to publications. And, unlike a column, a comic strip is pretty much editor-proof. Newspapers can't delete, add, or rearrange anything I do. I'm in complete control.

Actually, I lied when I said newspapers can't change anything I do. The *Washington Blade* doesn't permit swearing or references to certain body parts in their newspaper, so I provide them with a self-bowdlerized alternative when one of my strips contains a naughty word. I feel sheepish about knuckling under to this silly policy, but it doesn't seem worth making a fuss over. Sometimes, as in this 1996 scene, it's my own choice to use stray punctuation instead of saying "fuck." But what the *Blade* objected to here was the epithet "asshole," as well as the extension of Lois's middle finger, which they requested permission to retract.

Revised version

defending lesbian liberty for twenty years

**National Center for Lesbian Rights
1977-1997**

Original version

Revised version

Working with committees often involves last-minute changes. Someone at the National Center for Lesbian Rights decided Mo looked too dour in this 1997 T-shirt design. I didn't have time to work on it, so I let them paste a smile on her face.

Occasionally, however, I get commissioned to do work for a magazine or an organization, and I have to work with an editor (or worse yet, a committee) to come up with an approved cartoon. When this happens, my smug sense of autonomy is shot to smithereens.

It's always an ego boost to be invited to create a cartoon, but after I stop gloating, mental paralysis sets in. What if I can't do what this editor thinks I can? And what exactly *does* this editor think I can do? I lose touch with my own strengths in my feverish attempt to conform to what I expect is expected of me. It's a good thing I'm able to work independently most of the time because I'm a quivering wreck when I'm working for someone else.

This condition worsens when I'm being asked to write on an assigned topic— usually something neutral and uncomplicated like breast cancer, abortion, or antigay violence. I frequently write about topical issues in "Dykes To Watch Out For," but without the narrative of the ongoing comic strip to buoy them up, weighty themes tend to sink like lead balloons. It's one thing to discuss breast cancer within the story of Jezanna's mother's illness, and quite another to lecture people from a bus placard about the neccessity of doing monthly self-exams. Even when I use my familiar characters, it's hard not to come across with the indoctrinating tone of *Reefer Madness*.

It is true, though, that I *do* love to lecture. A review once called my comic strip "didactic," and I took it as a compliment. But I've gradually learned that the most effective propaganda is the subtlest. The pieces in this chapter get more and more successful at weaving their messages into the story instead of relying on Mo to deliver the information in a rant.

Commissioned cartoons almost always end up being rewarding and character-building experiences for me. But character-building experiences are not generally known for their frolicsome, carefree quality. Working with editors is just that—work.

Conspiring with other cartoonists, however, has given me a sense of play unparalleled in my life since grade school art class. At the end of this chapter are a few collaborations I've worked on. My favorite is the "The Party," a cartoon "jam" that I was invited to participate in with five other people. A jam is an improvisational cartoon that one artist starts, then passes on to the next, and so on. I actually felt more creative freedom working on this jam than I typically do working alone on my own strip: there were absolutely no rules. Characters didn't have to stay in character, the plot didn't have to make sense, and there's not a socially responsible message in the whole thing. But perhaps most exhilarating of all, I had no control whatsoever over the final product.

These panels are from a comic I did in 1988 for *Strip AIDS U.S.A.*, an AIDS benefit comic book. Me at my didactic, heavy-handed, statistic-spewing finest.

This strip was commissioned by the Fenway Community Health Center's Breast Health Project in 1993, and ran on bus placards in Boston under the heading, "Breasts To Watch Out For." It's an educational strip, but that doesn't excuse the preachy tone.

This piece was commissioned by the *Advocate* in 1988. I was thrilled to be doing something for a national publication, and astounded by the three hundred bucks they paid me for it. It's a very dated strip. No one could get away with these stock overgeneralizations about lesbians and gay men now, but I was young and naive and those were more innocent times.

189

The *Advocate* liked "a few things gay men have always wanted to know...," and shortly after it was published, Mark Thompson, one of the editors, invited me to do a monthly serial cartoon for the magazine. I obliged with "Servants To The Cause," a strip about the staff of the *Ten Percent Tribune.* I was working as production manager of a gay and lesbian newspaper in Minneapolis at the time, so I had access to plenty of material.

Eric, the Radical Faerie, quickly became the anchor of the strip. He's sort of a cross between Mo, Sparrow, and Lois—a politically committed, astrology-dependent voluptuary.

I would send Mark Thompson drafts of the strip for his approval. He almost always pushed me to come up with a snappier punchline. As I did revisions, I'd grumble to myself that punchlines were a typically male and inherently oppressive formal device. But my writing improved nonetheless.

I have a particular fondness for this 1990 episode of "Servants To The Cause" because it's so prescient. Almost everything Eric saw in his dream has already happened. I think it also nicely encapsulates a lot of my own complex feelings about assimilation and identity. As deeply as I yearn to be just like everyone else, I can't imagine a worse fate.

The last episode of "Servants To The Cause" was #19. In 1990, the *Advocate* changed their format and dropped my strip, as well as Tim Barela's wonderful "Leonard and Larry." I was relieved, more than anything else, because I was getting really burnt out producing a "Servants" episode on top of two "Dykes" installments every month.

This strip was created in 1990 for *Choices, A Pro-Choice Benefit Comic*. As usual, faced with an assigned topic, I clutched. Instead of writing about an aspect of the abortion issue that I had an emotional response to, I tried to write what I thought the editors wanted. The result is this dull, namby-pamby call to "work in coalition." Sheesh.

I did this piece in the summer of 1991 for *Out/Look*, a short-lived but vibrant national gay and lesbian quarterly. Robin Stevens, the editor, wanted a cartoon "review" of the infamous National Lesbian Conference held in Atlanta that spring. I hadn't attended the conference myself. For some reason I couldn't get it up to spend the time or money, and ultimately I think my sadly counterrevolutionary apathy comes through in the cartoon.

I felt really pressured to come up with a piercing insight into the cultural significance of the conference because *Out/Look* was a serious intellectual journal. Robin supplied me with news articles, speeches from the plenaries, and a long list of suggestions. But the more I learned, the less I could think of to say. My combined feelings of intimidation and boredom were a deadly combination, and I probably never should have agreed to take on the assignment.

My experience with "The Post-Mortem" was a walk in the park compared to the crisis of confidence I suffered with "Ordinary People." I got invited to contribute a cartoon to a *Village Voice* supplement called "The Year in Comix: 1992 Drawn and Quartered." My problem this time was the audience. All kinds of people read the *Voice*, not just queer ones. Did that mean I should write about something non-lesbian? On the other hand, did that mean that I *should* write about a lesbian topic because why else would they have asked me to contribute?

I eventually decided to stick with what I knew best and showed my characters having one of their trademark conversations. But without the context of who these women are, the piece was oddly incomplete. If this were one of my regular "DTWOF" strips, the exchange between Mo, Ginger, and Lois would have been just a part, or a subplot, of a longer story.

I had another occasion for panic when Robin Morgan called me about doing a full-page cartoon for *Ms. Magazine* in 1992. This time my paralysis stemmed not only from anxiety about working for a different audience than I was used to, but also from awe of my editor. I was terrified of making an unforgiveable political faux pas in front of a big-time feminist like Robin Morgan. I overcompensated and did an absurd amount of research.

All my strife was worth it, though, because of how this piece improved my relationship with my mother. After her initial spasm of horror when "Dykes To Watch Out For" began running in newspapers, my mom pretty much ignored my cartooning career. But *Ms.*, unlike *Gay Community News*, was something she had heard of and could display in public. And it didn't hurt that she was even more impressed with Robin Morgan than I was. My mom has taken my work very seriously ever since, and occasionally helps me out with research. Actually, the "Scarlet Sin" lipstick color on the bottom left figure of this page was her idea.

195

Ms. liked the "style supplement," so Robin Morgan commissioned me to do another full-page cartoon, this time for the back cover of their twentieth anniversary issue in 1993. The C.R. group reunion was her idea. I didn't feel very confident writing about this older generation of women, but various staff members at *Ms.* helped out with ideas.

I modeled the page on the "behind the scenes" cartoons that *Mad Magazine* used to do—big, single-panel tableaux of an office or an airport or a department store, with all kinds of activities going on. It was surprisingly tricky to compose. The final art was in color.

overexposed

© 1993 BY ALISON BECHDEL

I did one last cartoon for Robin Morgan at *Ms.*, but she left the magazine before they could run it. The piece got lost in the transition to the new editor, and I eventually collected a kill fee. It was just as well, though, because I wrote the piece at the height of the *lesbian chic* craze in 1993 and it was stale practically before the ink was dry.

My propaganda skills had improved by the time I did this 1994 piece, designed as part of a poster for the New York City Gay and Lesbian Anti-Violence Project. The educational message of the strip doesn't hit you over the head quite as bluntly as it did in the pro-choice, AIDS, and breast cancer strips earlier in this chapter.

Rather than sounding like they're reading from cue cards, the characters convey the required information fairly naturally in their conversation. I think there's an emotional resonance here, too, that the earlier pieces lack. Maybe that's because I've never personally had AIDS, breast cancer, or an abortion. But I have gotten slugged in the eye on the street.

Leslie Feinberg commissioned this strip for hir book *Transgender Warriors*. The only direction s/he gave me was that the piece should relate to the chapter about how women's oppression and trans oppression intersect.

The strip is a tad heavy-handed, but I think it gets a lot across in a few panels. I wanted to show that there are many different ways of being a woman, none of which even remotely resembles the glyph on the restroom door.

Harvey Pekar is the king of auto-biographical comics. His comic book series, *American Splendor*, chronicles his life as a file clerk at a V.A. hospital in Cleveland with mind-numbing naturalism. I've loved his work since a friend introduced me to it in college. Harvey doesn't draw, but hires different cartoonists to illustrate his stories.

I got to meet Harvey and his wife Joyce Brabner, who's also a comic book writer, on a trip to Cleveland in 1989. We all went out to breakfast together, and at one point Harvey started scribbling on a notepad. He was transcribing the conversation of the two guys at the next table, I realized. Then he pushed the sheet of notes over to me and said, "Here. You can illustrate this if you want." He had the dialogue all mapped out in panels with stick figures.

Working with someone I admired so much was a little nervewracking, but not as much as I would have expected. I felt a natural affinity with Harvey's style and really enjoyed drawing these old guys.

200

American Splendor #14

American Splendor #14

I got to work with another cartoonist hero in 1991, when I was asked to collaborate with Howard Cruse on an illustration for the *Village Voice*. I had been friends with Howard for a couple of years at that point, but it was still a thrill to be on the same page with him. The article we were illustrating was about different generations of gay men and lesbians, so we drew this "homo timeline" of people from the '60s, '70s, '80s, and '90s.

After seeing how my art practically disappeared next to Howard's, I started drawing thicker outlines.

THE PARTY

©95

A CARTOON JAM BY:
(IN ORDER OF APPEARANCE)

1 Jennifer Camper
2 Howard Cruse
3 Diane DiMassa
4 Rupert Kinnard
5 Alison Bechdel
6 Ivan Velez Jr.

Since this piece was a group effort, I'm including marginal comments from each of the five other artists about what it was like to do this jam.

"With Jennifer, the jam's instigator, keeping the ball in play, we joined in innocently, not realizing how quickly our civilized veneers would be stripped away. Diane suffered less from that indignity than the rest of us, of course, since the land of Hothead wasn't highly veneered, civilization-wise, to begin with. And Rupert must be given credit for nobly trying to divert us from base impulses with a strategic geographical relocation (a futile ploy, since this just isn't the sort of party folks are easily pried away from). Poor, earnest Mo was caught in the crossfire—no thanks to Alison, who (once liberated from the constraints of DTWOF continuity) seemed as ready to see under-garments fly as the rest of us."

Howard Cruse, creator of "Wendel" and author of Stuck Rubber Baby

203

"Doing a jam is a free-for-all. Everyone is uninhibited because there's no structure or storyline to worry about: you don't know what's coming next and you can be as ridiculous as you want, all the time snickering because you picture the next person having to deal with what you just did. It's great to share the burden of writing with the others, and to watch the strip deteriorate into absurdity. I love these people!"

Diane DiMassa, creator of "Hothead Paisan"

"I continue to be amazed at how rewarding it is to collaborate with other creative people. Participating in this jam was the most fun I've had recently that didn't involve shortness of breath. I've always loved the idea of positioning different cartooning styles side-by-side. The fact that I had to endure other cartoonists depicting my characters doing things that I could never imagine them doing was quite the humbling experience. I'm waiting for the day of the great payback!"

Rupert Kinnard a.k.a. Professor I.B. Gittendowne has been spewing forth "Cathartic Comics," featuring the Brown Bomber and Diva Touché Flambé, since 1976.

"I love jams because it's a chance to get out of that solitary, cartoonist-working-in-a-vacuum state of mind, and to create with people whose work I admire. Drawing another artist's characters is a very intimate thing—you learn a lot about how other people draw, and you have control over their characters. But in a jam nobody has complete control over the plot, so it is humbling to relinquish it to others. I really enjoyed watching this story unfold. I'm impressed that the sum of our individual twisted, wacko panels creates an even more twisted, wacko comic."

Jennifer Camper, creator of *Rude Girls and Dangerous Women* and "subGURLZ"

"It was pure hell from start to finish."

Ivan Velez Jr.'s comic book credits include such tasty morsels as *Tales of the Closet*, and the mainstream delectables *Blood Syndicate, Static, Holocaust,* and *Ghost Rider.*

Chapter six
Audience Participation

I used to say I would draw "DTWOF" even if no one else were reading it. Not because I had such an overwhelming need to create it, but because I had an overwhelming need to see it—to see my particular queer progressive slice of life reflected back to me. But now I'm not so sure I could keep drawing without an audience. The peculiar reciprocity that has developed between the strip and its readers provides me with an essential fuel. Without it, I don't know if I'd have the energy to keep the story going.

Cartooning, like writing, often demands monastic bouts of solitude. But at the same time, I have a creatively interactive relationship with my readers. While a novelist might get letters from readers about a recent book, those responses never influence the novel itself—it's already a fait accompli. My comic strip, however, is never accompli: it's literally endless. Serial episodes appear in newspapers every two weeks, and thus I have the dubious privilege of receiving constant feedback about the progress of the narrative. Being an assertive, egalitarian lot, my audience does not scruple to let me know what's wrong (or right, for that matter) with the strip, or to inform me of directions and issues that they think I should be exploring.

I've always been touched by my readers' proprietary attitude toward "DTWOF" and, in my turn, have not scrupled to shamelessly appropriate their suggestions. A guy at my gym kept bugging me to put a gay man in the strip, so I introduced Carlos. A bisexual reader thought I should make Naomi bisexual, so I did. After a review illustrated how unnaturally well my characters got along by remarking that none of them were even allergic to one anothers' pets, I obligingly had Sydney develop a sudden sensitivity to cat dander.

I'm not so easily led all of the time. I've steadfastly resisted many requests to reunite Mo and Harriet. I ignored the calls for Rafael to be born a girl. And I wasn't convinced that Mo and Sydney should start exploring S/M, as a woman pulled me aside at a conference to suggest, even though I agreed that their initials are curiously symbolic.

But whether or not I actually make use of my readers' propositions, they constitute a vital dialogue for me, evidence that all the long, lonely hours of inking to *Music Through the Night* on N.P.R. are not in vain. That people not only read my strip but are sufficiently engaged with it to suggest that Sparrow think about going to massage school is all the success I could ever hope for.

I admit that occasionally I get a little irked by the myriad requests. But mostly I consider them an honor, especially the ones asking me to introduce a character just like the person writing the letter. If "DTWOF" weren't already a reasonably diverse and hospitable place I don't think they'd bother. (Maybe I'm wrong. Maybe the guy who writes "Family Circus" gets a lot of calls for transgender characters.) Even though it's impossible to include all the different kinds of people I'm asked to, I try to represent as many as I can. Yes, this makes for a slightly more utopian community than most of us experience in real life, and I have been accused (albeit in a mainstream publication) of being "racially diverse to a fault," but so what? I know from experience the surprised thrill of catching a reflection of yourself in the cultural mirror—even if it's just a cartoon—when you're used to vampiric invisibility.

A letter I received in 1989 said: "I always feel really validated and restored to sanity whenever I read your stuff. Something about the power of having dyke culture in all its intelligence, sensitivity, variety, and courage mirrored back to me." If that culture weren't there to reflect in the first place, there wouldn't be any "DTWOF." There's a symbiotic relationship, an intimate collusion between the characters in my comic strip and the intelligent, sensitive, courageous, and ever-increasingly varied three-dimensional characters who inspire them. In fact, much of my mail sounds like it was written by Mo herself, as you can see for yourself in the following sampling of letters I've received over the past fifteen years. Age, gender, and other distinguishing features are noted where relevant.

Cartoonophilia

"I'll bet you didn't realize there are dykes out here who actually felt the need to masturbate after watching Harriet and Mo's first night together."

"My patience has finally paid off. Mo is now single once again, and I am free to make my move on her in a politically correct manner. I know that I am perfect for her. Mo needs the influence of a wild woman to help her shadow to come leaping out. I don't want to belittle the splendid job her therapist is doing, I just think I could speed things up a bit. It's my plan to tickle Mo into letting her little sphincter have some much needed rest."

"DO YOU HAVE ANY IDEA WHAT IT'S LIKE TO HAVE A CRUSH ON A CARTOON CHARACTER?!!?"

"You're probably gonna think this is strange, but I'd love to go out with some of the lesbians that you draw! Some of your drawings are pretty hot, especially Lois."

"You could have Mo go on some blind dates with readers. Just a thought."

"I am in love with Mo. I know she's two-dimensional and in a relationship with Harriet, but I can't help myself. I'm hopelessly enamoured. She's just so cranky and cute. I simply must meet her. Maybe Harriet could go out of the country on urgent business and you could write me in for a strip or two. No pressure."

Uh...have you mentioned this to your therapist?

"Many times I've thought that if I could, I would crawl right into the strip and live there."

"It's like these women are friends of mine. Weirdly, I sometimes feel I am closer to them than my real friends."

"I'd rather be a Dyke To Watch Out For than live in my very own life. I've started discussing what's going on in the strip with my friends, who get confused about who's a character and who might be a new person in my life."

"Sometimes I think I know them better than my real friends, but let's not analyze that. If you would, please pass along to Mo that this dyke thinks she looks just spiffin' in her new bathing suit, pale flabby thighs and all. Besides, bathing suits are clearly a tool of the patriarchy, designed to make women disgusted with their own bodies. Everyone I know looks much better naked than they do in a bathing suit."

"The three of us are sitting around the table debating the future of Mo and Harriet's relationship. Carla says they're doomed because Mo's so flaky and a twit. Robin says of course they'll stay together, and I say that it's all up to you. Then Carla said, "What does *she* have to do with it?"

I'm not a lesbian, but...

"I am writing to tell you how much I enjoy your cartoon. It's so funny because it is true. In case you're wondering, I am a gay male, 34, semi-employed as a bartender in a local leather bar. Underneath the chaps, I am really a shy, retiring bookworm."

AH! YOU'VE FINALLY REALIZED WHAT A **CROCK** QUEER STUDIES IS, AND YOU'RE DONATING ALL THESE BOOKS TO THE CONCERNED WOMEN FOR AMERICA RUMMAGE SALE.

SADLY, NO. THIS IS ABOUT HALF THE READING I NEED TO DO THIS SUMMER FOR MY BOOK. THE PRESSURE'S REALLY ON FOR ME TO PUBLISH.

"Ideologically and every other way we're probably as unalike as could be imagined (in the interest of full disclosure, I'm the happily married father of 4, a right-wing conservative Christian, Republican precinct captain, etc.). Believe it or not, there's far from unanimity of opinion out here on the right wing about Jerry Falwell, Concerned Women of America, etc. I was particularly tickled by the thought of donating Lesbian Studies books to the CWA rummage sale."

"I just had to write and tell you about our wedding/union/whatever ceremony. We are an opposite-sex couple of your fairly typical lefty-p.c. persuasion. Yup, a pair of wannabes. That's why I wanted Mo at my, uh, wedding. So we set up a sort of altar, and upon it were things representing people who couldn't be at our ceremony. I added my little Mo button to the arrangement. I suppose that by now you know your characters have a life of their own. I just thought you might like to know where they show up on their days off from DTWOF."

"I am a longtime fan of DTWOF, and incidentally a heterosexual male. I enjoy the in-depth treatment of a particular subculture of which I am mostly ignorant, but this element exerts no more special fascination than it does in an essay by Tom Wolfe detailing the lives of Vietnam fighter pilots. To expound an old cliché from freshman lit courses, the greatest art achieves universality by rendering with great fidelity a specific milieu. We are all in this late 20th-century American craziness together."

"I bought *Spawn of DTWOF*, or rather, my husband bought it for me for Christmas, and I LOVED it."

"Recently I was stuck in traffic and remembered that I had *Spawn of DTWOF* in my backpack. So I got it out and started reading it, holding it up to keep an eye on the light. Then I got beeped by the car behind me. I looked, but the light was still red! Turns out two sisters were behind me giving me the thumbs-up sign! They thought it was really funny. Maybe it's because I'm a bearish gay man and they thought I should be reading 'Leonard and Larry' instead (which I also like)."

"My dad liked the erotic note cards. So did I. I think what I am called is a dyke daddy. Do you think Mo would go for me? (Just kidding, ha-ha.) I really wanted to see your presentation, but my girlfriend said I would not be welcome plus I had to report for a maneuver the next morning." (male Marine just back from Desert Storm)

"I'm not a lesbian, just a middle-aged straight grandmother, but I'm a fan of comic strips and like to think that they can change people's ideas of what's accepted as normal and usual."

"For a while in the '80s, I was walking around thinking lesbians were a higher form of life. Now I know they're just more fun." (from a man)

As part of my schlock business, I once printed up a set of note cards with some of the preparatory pencil sketches from Mo and Harriet's big sex scene. They were the only product I ever tried to sell that was an utter failure. (Well, except for those leaky water bottles.) Obviously, I wasn't marketing them to the right audience.

So many women, so little space...

HEY, THANKS FOR INCLUDING JILLIAN'S WORK TONIGHT. I'M GONNA TELL MY FRIEND BIFF TO SEND YOU SOME OF HIS POEMS. HE'S BEEN WRITING **GREAT** STUFF ABOUT HIS FEMALE-TO-MALE TRANSITIONING.

UH... BIFF?

"How about a nice old dyke in your strip sometime? So the kiddies will know we're around."

"How about a bearded dyke character?"

"I'd like to ask that you include more of Jillian in future strips. I would enjoy seeing more of her experiences as a new female, and although I certainly don't expect the strip to revolve around her, having her as a continuing character would be, in my opinion, a definite plus for the series. You also made reference in a recent strip to a female-to-male transsexual named Biff. I can't help but think that a part of your readership would enjoy seeing him as well."

"I need to make one suggestion for future projects. I haven't yet seen myself or my peers represented in your cartoons. I look for a dyke in a wheelchair, or a blind dyke with a cane or a dog, or a deaf dyke signing to another dyke. We're all in the community too, and sometimes we're participants in some pretty comic situations."

"I'm looking in the comix for a character like myself. So if you haven't already, would you please put in a 40-year-old woods-witch-healer type, who goes from het to bi to lesbo?"

"There is a lot of diversity among Asian American lesbians and from what I can tell, your characters are mainly East Asians, i.e. Chinese, Japanese, and possibly Korean. Perhaps there can be a South Asian, Southeast Asian or Pacific Islander lesbian included. While I understand you must get plenty of requests to include the diversity of the lesbian community, I thought I would also throw in my two cents."

"In *on our backs*, you said that there weren't any bisexuals in your strip because you don't know that many of us. How many more do you have to meet? It seems to me that you try to show the women's community in all its diversity, for better or worse, and this feels like a painful, unfair, and unnecessary omission."

"More Jewish Dykes!! 'We're here, We're queer, We're not just eating Matzoh!' I would love to see a Sephardic dyke active in coalition with Palestinian women. And more appearances by Naomi. Also, could Mo please get 1) more likeable/less pesky and 2) further along in therapy? Right now, she's kind of a Dyke To Put UP With."

"Please get some Jews, out Jews, into this community you've created. I don't want much, mind you. I'd like them to be dealing with their consciences about Palestine and Israel and the grief between U.S. Jews and African Americans in these tough times."

"Have you ever considered introducing a Christian dyke?"

"Thank God you gave Jezanna a woman. It was about time! Heavyset black women need love too. We would like to see more activity going on with Ginger, Sparrow, and the other women of color. We like the others, but *we* need the spotlight too."

"Hey, I've got a fabulous idea for a new character for "Servants To The Cause." He's Eric's new boyfriend. He's also a radical faerie, about 25, tall, thin, very cute, brown hair (after two years as a blond), and struggling valiantly and courageously and successfully against an AIDS diagnosis! If you need a model, I'd be happy to send some photos of myself."

Soon after I received the letter about bi-sexuality, Naomi broke rank.

215

"At the risk of being a pushy stage mom, I am sending you photos of my Golden Retriever, Gertrude. I hope this isn't too forward of me, but thought you might consider the possibility of better representing my life as a radical dyke dog owner."

"My roommate has an idea for another new character. She says that you need to add a visual artist to the cast. When Mo was organizing that series of readings, there was a whole parade of various writers, but the only visual artist that I can think of was Malika, who really was a major babe (which seems like an odd thing to say about a fictional character) but anyway, my roommate would be happy to model for you."

"Most of the women in the strip have semi-normal jobs and we think a dyke that works as a mechanic would be great to read about. Think about it and let us know." (from workers at a dyke garage)

"We are both police officers and find that departments across the country are recruiting gays and lesbians. One of your characters is looking for a job. How about having her join the local gendarmes?"

Malika pursuing her art

Just a small request...

"What about Mo having a ménage a trois with Hothead and Tank Girl? I think she's ready."

"How about a t-shirt sporting the dykes doing the Boot Scoot Boogie? And is Sparrow ever going to go to massage school? I'm a massage therapist, and it takes one to know one."

"I think Mo's therapist is too passive. She just sits back and listens and occasionally asks a 'leading' question. Just like the patriarchal Freudians. Mo needs a feminist therapist with an egalitarian approach who will empower her and enhance her self-esteem."

"I think Mo needs a new shirt. She's been wearing that striped turtleneck for years. Shall I put her name on the mailing list for the Travis Place catalog?"

The Travis Place catalog featured all sorts of sensible cotton clothing for women. It wasn't an overtly lesbian enterprise, but its readily identifiable underwear models made for provocative bathtub reading.

"Here's a request worthy of Mo. Would you give some strip time to the boycott against FLAV-R-PAC, Santiam, & Steinfeld's brands that has been called by Oregon's farmworker union?"

A FORTUITOUS HOLE IN HER JEANS PROVIDED CELESTE WITH THE MEANS TO ENJOY A CARESS WITH NO NEED TO UNDRESS WHILE SHE THRILLED TO HER FAVORITE SCENES.

"I am open to many sexual deviations, but not really amused by a woman masturbating with a child sitting right behind her. Or anyone really. Get it together Alison, did you really do this cartoon??! While we're at it, we would like to see more butch/femme. Thanks for everything."

Some suggestions arrive addressed directly to a character, like these two to Clarice back when she was on the verge of having an affair with Ginger.

"What the fuck is wrong with you, girl? Don't you know the difference between love and lust by now? Is one night of 'gravity' worth breaking Toni's heart? Get your brain out from between your legs. The only ginger you should be eating right now is the spice."

"To Clarice, re: DTWOF #33. DON'T DO IT!"

"So when is Mo gonna get laid? Hopefully not until after I do. When will Sparrow reclaim her cultural heritage by going to acupuncture school, or at least by going to acupuncture? When will the Dykes start getting massage and when will you break out of social work and chiropractic as the sole Lesbian healing modalities?"

"How come money isn't mentioned in your strip? I'd like to see who is irresponsible, who messes up with it, why and how, and who is managing hers well. Are Emma or Thea constantly boasting about the bargains they get? Is Lois broke? Is Mo's parsimony with what little money she probably earns yet another of her irritating and endearing concerns? Doesn't anybody impose upon Toni's accounting knowledge, and if so, does she resent it?"

"You can't let Mo go out with Sydney. AAAUGH!!"

Internationale

"It is really a pleasure to see Alison Bechdel in France during our office hours. Thanks god she is a lesbian." (e-mail, presumably regarding my web site, since I haven't been in France recently, either during or after office hours)

"I decided to write to you immediately, because we are of the same shoes for me. I believe in struggle continuous. I love you wholeheartedly assuming you are a boy." (Nigeria)

"Forgive me for being so forward as advising that you should consider showing your work here, but I believe it is of such high value, wonderfully drawn and very humourous and it would be a pity that South Africa does not get to share in your humour."

"I'm not sure if your strips are primarily aimed at young gay men in north London, but they have an audience here anyway. I've just realised I look like Mo. Any chance of writing-in an early 20s, gay, British brother for her?"

"I am a lesbian feminist living in Osaka, Japan. This is the first day I connect Internet, and this is the first e-mail I send. In Japan, our situation is very hard, but we are living powerfully with our good friends."

"Toni et Clarice, j'aime leurs complicités et ce grand amour. C'est vraiment le couple idéal et je les souhaites grand bonheur et longue vie." (France)

"All Finnish dykes love your cartoons!" (Finland)

"Now I found your fifth volume here in Madrid at Berkana, the first gay bookstore in this country. Seeing your newest book made me so happy, seeing how my country changes with a symbol: being able to get the cartoon." (Spain)

Check one:
❑ Mo's gay British brother
❑ FTM Mo

Vintage

"You're a fine example of an amazon with womyn-pride." (1984)

"Love your humor! It's so very lesbian." (1986)

"As a 35-year-old lesbian feminist long involved in the

feinist anti-pornography and anti-S/M movement, we would probably disagree around some issues, but I thoroughly admire the strength of your words and the clarity of your commitment to women." (1987)

Yes, as a matter of fact, I am spying on you.

"Your 'Serial Monogamy' was so insightful! Have you been spying on my failed relationships or what? You got the dialogue down pat. Page 117 [*DTWOF: The Sequel*] happened seven years ago with me and my ex. You met her at your slideshow with the woman she left me for."

"Thanks for having Naomi come out (more or less) as bisexual. Her lover David looks exactly like one of my exes."

"We have a Mo and a Lois living near us!"

"I swear to GOD I am living with Harriet. I SWEAR. This woman found out she had gotten fired by her double-dipped born-again boss at work and didn't even THROW anything. She made BROWNIES."

"Just had this psychic experience with your strip. My lover left tonight for a Victory Fund reception in New York after just having met with her staff about a report which they're preparing for Beijing. It's kind of amazing how much (my partner) looks like Ellen. Hope she doesn't fall in love with someone else. We're moving in together in October."

"I used to say I could find out how my life would turn out by reading the latest 'Dykes' book. Needless to say, I was shocked and saddened to read about Mo and Harriet splitting up. Especially since I met my 'Harriet' four years ago, and

we're getting 'married.' She's kind of built like Harriet, too."
(from a woman named Mo)

"You know the scene in the last book where Mo is en route to the March on Washington, and everyone else has fallen asleep with their various sweeties, and you just see Mo, still awake, suspended in this lonely spotlight? I love that because I've been there. I don't get to see anyone sharing that situation with me when I read 'Calvin & Hobbes' or 'Doonesbury' or George Eliot." (Author's note: I didn't know she wrote a comic strip.)

"I died laughing when I saw your 'morning person' cartoon because the first time I spent the night with my lover she was up at 5:30 a.m. baking scones and *singing*, fer goddess' sake!"

Youth wants to know

"I have read all of your books about dykes to watch out for my favorite characters are Lois, she is funny, Mo, she whines a lot, Sparrow and Clarice. Is Mo based on you? In 3 days school starts and I am not excited about that because I have the most homophobic person in my class." (age 11)

"I'm a 14-year-old girl of unknown sexual orientation. I read the Comic News to find out what's going on in the news because good humorists often hit reality right on the nose. It is comforting to know that lesbians are just as abnormal and confused and happy and life-seeking as 'normal' people. Whatever way the chips fall for me, I'll continue to read your column."

"I just started fifth grade and it's pretty good. I'm at a new school and I'm making a lot of friends (I don't think any of

Yes! It is a mezuzah! (a small case containing biblical inscriptions that observant Jews affix to their doorposts). In my cartoon, Thea's mezuzah is nearly microscopic, but I wanted it to be there and I wanted it to be accurate. I wasn't sure which direction it was supposed to point, so I actually persuaded my girlfriend to call up her Rabbi and ask him. This probably wins the prize for the most effort expended on the least amount of ink, but the fact that someone noticed it made me feel like it was all worthwhile.

them read 'Dykes to Watch Out For')."

"Unfortunately I have the chicken pox right now but I have practically memorized *Dykes To Watch Out For: The Sequel.*" (age 10)

"It's me, the dykomaniac. I thought the 1994 calendar was brill. You introduced lots of new characters. The 'Where's Mo?' section was too easy though. Do you like my joined-up (cursive) writing?" (age 9, U.K.)

What was that?

"Your cartoon 'Sodomy Blues' [*More DTWOF*] cracked me up so much, you made my day. I'll have to look up 'antediluvian' in the dictionary, though."

"In episode #228, who or what is 'Foucauldian'? We have enclosed a self-addressed stamped envelope for your convenience. "

"In the strip where Sydney goes over to apologize to Thea, was that a mezuzah on Thea and Maxine's doorjamb?"

Well, it beats the hell out of The Well of Loneliness

"Yours was the first lesbian publication I had ever read and enjoyed. I found it in my school library."

"I've just begun the coming out process and am slowly locating bits and pieces of our local community, but it's good to have your strip to help get me through things like my physician telling me to find god! So, thanks huge bunches!"

"I finally came out to myself. Was I ever going to find a job being queer? Was my 'best' friend from high school every going to call me again? Then I found this one lonely comic book in the college bookstore. Suddenly I began to feel, well, complete again."

"Before I had any real dyke friends of my own, I discovered your book. And then I knew that there were Moes and Harriets and Sparrows out there that I simply hadn't met yet."

Firebrand Books is an award-winning feminist and lesbian publishing house committed to producing quality work in a wide variety of genres by ethnically and racially diverse authors. Now in our thirteenth year, we have over ninety titles in print.

You can buy Firebrand titles at your bookstore, or order them directly from the publisher, 141 The Commons, Ithaca, New York 14850, (607) 272-0000.

A free catalog is available on request.